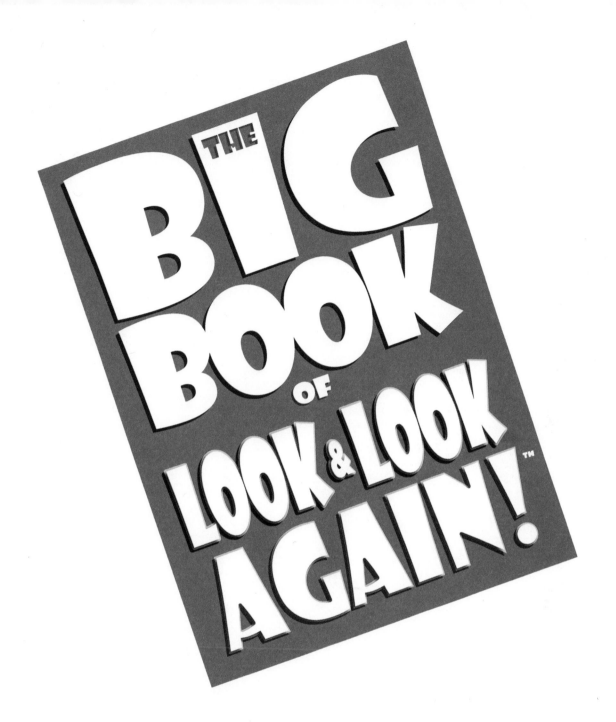

THE BIG BOOK OF LOOK & LOOK AGAIN!™

Tony Tallarico

Kidsbooks®

STRANGE-BUT-TRUE MYSTERIES

THE GIANT STATUES OF EASTER ISLAND

On Easter Sunday in 1722, Dutch Admiral Jacob Roggeveen sailed to a small island in the South Pacific. When he went ashore, he discovered more than 600 giant statues carved from stone, some of which were over 40 feet tall. In 1947, Thor Heyerdahl, a Norwegian archaeologist, led an expedition to try to find out how the statues got there.

LEARN ABOUT THE GIANT STATUES OF EASTER ISLAND
AS YOU LOOK FOR THESE FUN ITEMS:

- Artist
- Banana leaves
- Bone
- Carrot
- Drum
- Duck
- Flower
- Flying bat
- Football
- Graduate
- Guitar
- Key
- Ladder
- Mouse
- Owl
- Painted eggs (3)
- Party hats (2)
- Pelican
- Periscope
- Photographer
- Ring
- Rocking chair
- Skateboard
- Stars (3)
- Telescope
- Toucan
- Truck
- Unicorn
- Wagon
- Water bucket
- Witch

What was used to carve the statues? What was the name of Thor Heyerdahl's craft?

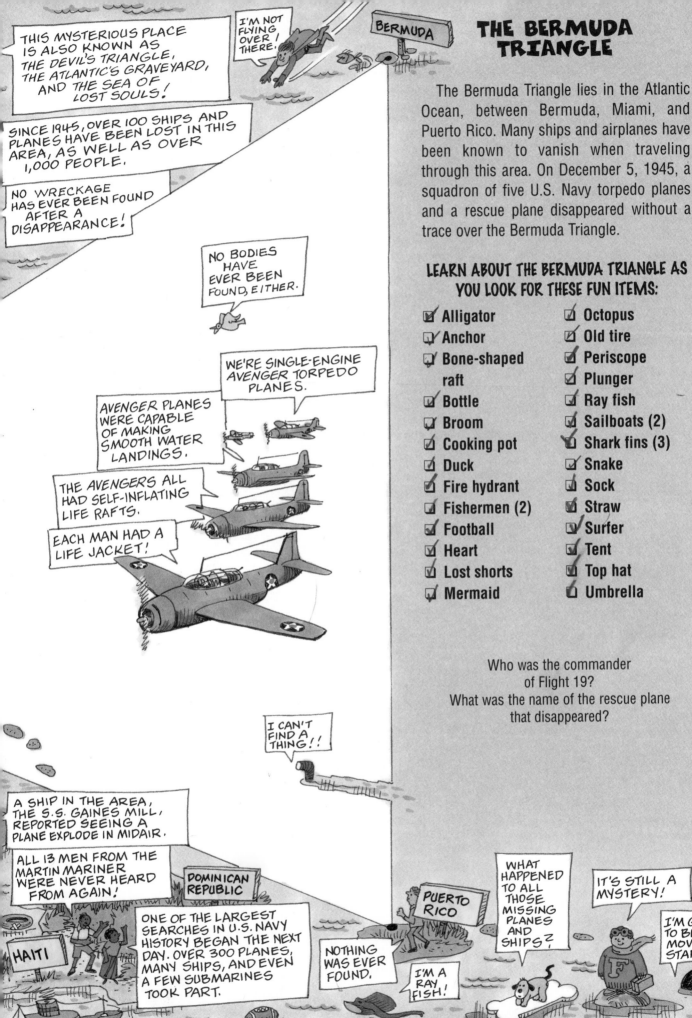

THE BERMUDA TRIANGLE

The Bermuda Triangle lies in the Atlantic Ocean, between Bermuda, Miami, and Puerto Rico. Many ships and airplanes have been known to vanish when traveling through this area. On December 5, 1945, a squadron of five U.S. Navy torpedo planes and a rescue plane disappeared without a trace over the Bermuda Triangle.

LEARN ABOUT THE BERMUDA TRIANGLE AS YOU LOOK FOR THESE FUN ITEMS:

- ☑ Alligator
- ☑ Anchor
- ☑ Bone-shaped raft
- ☑ Bottle
- ☑ Broom
- ☑ Cooking pot
- ☑ Duck
- ☑ Fire hydrant
- ☑ Fishermen (2)
- ☑ Football
- ☑ Heart
- ☑ Lost shorts
- ☑ Mermaid
- ☑ Octopus
- ☑ Old tire
- ☑ Periscope
- ☑ Plunger
- ☑ Ray fish
- ☑ Sailboats (2)
- ☑ Shark fins (3)
- ☑ Snake
- ☑ Sock
- ☑ Straw
- ☑ Surfer
- ☑ Tent
- ☑ Top hat
- ☑ Umbrella

Who was the commander of Flight 19?
What was the name of the rescue plane that disappeared?

THE LOCH NESS MONSTER

In 1933, a Scottish couple was driving along a new, modern road on the northern shore of Loch Ness. (*Loch* is the Scottish word for "lake.") Suddenly, their attention was drawn to the center of the lake. They later claimed that what they saw there was an enormous animal "rolling and plunging" in the water. Since that day, there have been more than 3,000 reported sightings of the Loch Ness monster.

LEARN ABOUT THE LOCH NESS MONSTER AS YOU LOOK FOR THESE FUN ITEMS:

- Astronaut
- Balloons (4)
- Bone
- Bucket
- Cameras (2)
- Clown
- Duck
- Fishbowl
- Flower
- Ghost
- Golfer
- Lost boot
- Mouse
- Mummy
- Net
- Note in a bottle
- Periscope
- Pig
- Sailboat
- Shorts
- Skateboard
- Star
- Sword
- Telescope
- Top hat
- Turtle

What is the monster's nickname?
How deep is Loch Ness?

STONEHENGE

Stonehenge is an ancient monument built on Salisbury Plain in Wiltshire, England. For centuries, scientists have puzzled over the circular arrangement of this group of huge, rough-cut stones and holes in the ground. Archaeologists believe that Stonehenge was shaped and positioned by a group of people more than 3,000 years ago, without the aid of modern tools and equipment. No one knows exactly how this was accomplished.

LEARN ABOUT STONEHENGE AS YOU LOOK FOR THESE FUN ITEMS:

- ☑ Arrow
- ☑ Bird
- ☑ Bone
- ☑ Book
- ☑ Clown face
- ☑ Cooking pot
- ☑ Crown
- ☑ Cupcake
- ☑ Duck
- ☑ Elephant
- ☑ Flower
- ☑ Flying saucer
- ☑ Football
- ☑ Guitar
- ☑ Handbag
- ☑ Horse
- ☑ Jogger
- ☑ Magic wand
- ☑ Merlin
- ☑ Palm tree
- ☑ Pencil
- ☑ Pickaxe
- ☑ Pig
- ☑ Rabbit
- ☑ Shovel
- ☑ Teapot
- ☑ Tennis racket
- ☑ Turtle
- ☑ Umbrella
- ☑ Worm

How many stones were used to build Stonehenge? How much do the heaviest stones weigh?

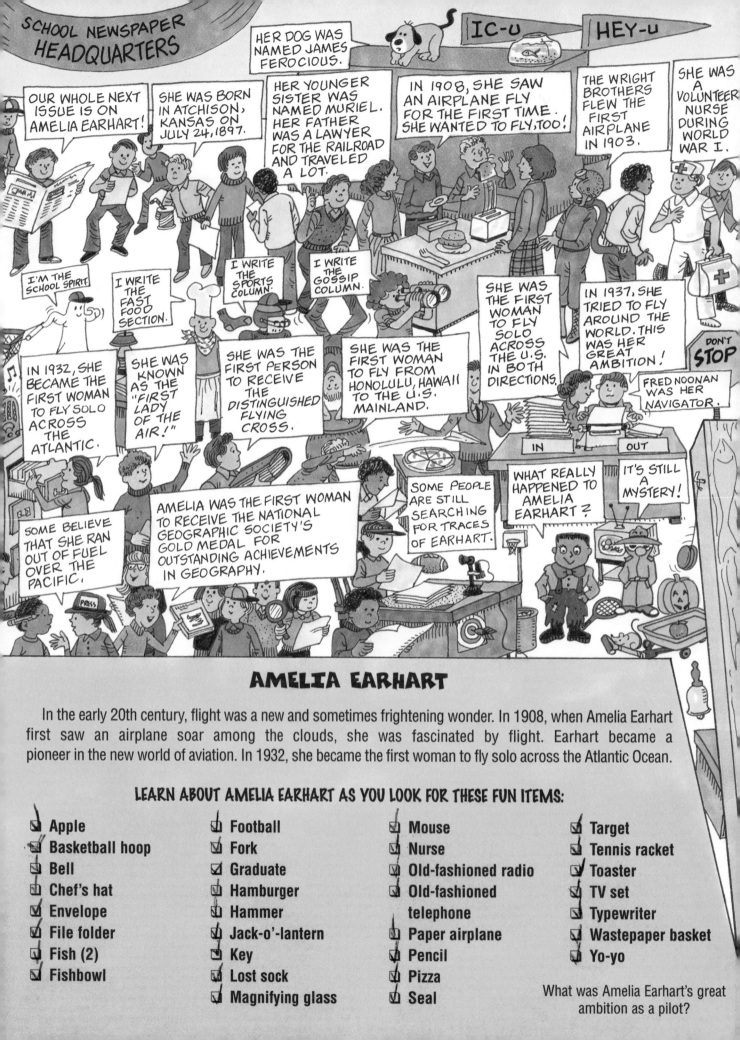

AMELIA EARHART

In the early 20th century, flight was a new and sometimes frightening wonder. In 1908, when Amelia Earhart first saw an airplane soar among the clouds, she was fascinated by flight. Earhart became a pioneer in the new world of aviation. In 1932, she became the first woman to fly solo across the Atlantic Ocean.

LEARN ABOUT AMELIA EARHART AS YOU LOOK FOR THESE FUN ITEMS:

- Apple
- Basketball hoop
- Bell
- Chef's hat
- Envelope
- File folder
- Fish (2)
- Fishbowl
- Football
- Fork
- Graduate
- Hamburger
- Hammer
- Jack-o'-lantern
- Key
- Lost sock
- Magnifying glass
- Mouse
- Nurse
- Old-fashioned radio
- Old-fashioned telephone
- Paper airplane
- Pencil
- Pizza
- Seal
- Target
- Tennis racket
- Toaster
- TV set
- Typewriter
- Wastepaper basket
- Yo-yo

What was Amelia Earhart's great ambition as a pilot?

AFTER THE WAR SHE ATTENDED COLUMBIA UNIVERSITY.

HER REAL LOVE WAS FLYING. SHE DROPPED OUT TO EARN MONEY FOR FLYING LESSONS.

SHE LEARNED TO FLY IN LOS ANGELES, CALIFORNIA AND IN 1928 BECAME THE FIRST WOMAN TO FLY ACROSS THE ATLANTIC OCEAN.

SHE FLEW WITH WILBUR STUNTZ AND LOUIS GORDON.

THE PLANE WAS NAMED "FRIENDSHIP!"

SHE WROTE A BOOK ABOUT HER FLIGHT AND LATER MARRIED HER PUBLISHER, GEORGE PUTNAM.

THEY FLEW IN A TWIN-ENGINE LOCKHEED 10-E ELECTRA AIRPLANE.

THE PLANE VANISHED SOMEWHERE BETWEEN NEW GUINEA AND HOWLAND ISLAND.

SOME THINK THAT THEY WERE SHOT DOWN BY THE JAPANESE WHO BELIEVED THEY WERE ON A SECRET SPY MISSION.

OTHERS BELIEVE HER PLANE RAN OUT OF FUEL AND WENT DOWN IN THE OCEAN.

THESE ARE GREAT COMIC STRIPS FOR OUR SCHOOL PAPER.

FREDDIE, LISA, AND LAURA ARE IN IT.

AMELIA EARHART'S FIRST ATTEMPT AT A ROUND-THE-WORLD FLIGHT ALMOST ENDED IN TRAGEDY. A TIRE BLOW-OUT WHILE TAXIING RESULTED IN CONSIDERABLE DAMAGE TO THE PLANE....

WHEN HER LOCKHEED ELECTRA WAS REPAIRED, MISS EARHART CHANGED HER DIRECTION. WITH NAVIGATOR FRED NOONAN, SHE TOOK OFF IN HER "FLYING LABORATORY," HEADING EASTWARD OUT OF MIAMI, ON THE GRAY MORNING OF JUNE 1, 1937.

WHEN AMELIA EARHART TOOK OFF ON HER ROUND-THE-WORLD FLIGHT, HER PLANE WAS WELL-EQUIPPED WITH RUBBER RAFTS, FLARES, AND OTHER SAFETY DEVICES. ENOUGH SURVIVAL EQUIPMENT TO MEET ALMOST ANY EVENTUALITY....

MISS EARHART FLEW A SOUTH EASTERLY ROUTE FROM MIAMI TO SOUTH AMERICA; THEN ON TO AFRICA. FROM THERE, SHE EASILY HOPPED TO INDIA AND ACROSS TO BATAVIA....

MIAMI
AFRICA
INDIA
SOUTH AMERICA
BATAVIA

HOWLAND ISLAND WAS TO BE THE LAST STOP BEFORE HONOLULU. A TINY, 2-MILE-SQUARE SPECK IN THE OCEAN.... A DIFFICULT TARGET FOR ANY PILOT....

AT 7:42 A.M., ON JULY 2, 1937, THE U.S. CUTTER ITASCA, WAITING AT HOWLAND ISLAND, RECEIVED THIS RADIO MESSAGE: "WE MUST BE ON YOU, BUT WE CANNOT SEE YOU. GAS IS RUNNING LOW. BEEN UNABLE TO REACH YOU BY RADIO...."

DURING THE NEXT DAYS, ONE OF THE LARGEST SEARCHES IN HISTORY TOOK PLACE. MEN, SHIPS, AND PLANES OF THREE NATIONS, INCLUDING JAPANESE AIRCRAFT, ENGAGED IN THE TREMENDOUS, EXHAUSTIVE HUNT....

THE OPERATION COST $1,000,000! THAT WAS 55 YEARS AGO. NOT ONE AUTHENTICATED CLUE TO THE FATE OF MISS EARHART, NAVIGATOR NOONAN, OR THEIR PLANE HAS EVER BEEN FOUND!

KING TUT'S CURSE

Howard Carter's 30-year search was over. On November 26, 1922, he stood before the entrance to the lost tomb of "the boy king," Tutankhamen *(too-tang-KAHM-un)*. Entering, Carter stared in disbelief at the gold, jewels, and other treasures before him. However, that day, a hawk—sacred symbol of pharaohs, the kings of ancient Egypt—was seen soaring above the tomb. Many people say that the hawk signalled the beginning of the pharaoh's curse.

LEARN ABOUT KING TUT'S CURSE AS YOU LOOK FOR THESE FUN ITEMS:

- ☑ Balloon
- ☑ Banana peel
- ☑ Broom
- ☑ Camel
- ☑ Crown
- ☑ Fish
- ☑ Flying bat
- ☑ Football player
- ☑ Ghost
- ☑ Horn
- ☑ Horseshoe
- ☑ Kite
- ☑ Lost medal
- ☑ Mouse
- ☑ Mummy and child
- ☑ Pencil
- ☑ Pizza deliveryman
- ☑ Sailor
- ☑ Sand
- ☑ Shovel
- ☑ Skier
- ☑ Snake
- ☑ Snowman
- ☑ Star
- ☑ Top hat
- ☑ Vase

What happened to Lord Carnarvon?
What was unusual about the scar on Tut's cheek?

ATLANTIS

The idea of a perfect world—one filled with beauty, peace, and happiness—had kept people searching for the lost island of Atlantis for centuries. Was Atlantis a real place, or just a myth of ancient Egypt made popular by Plato?

LEARN ABOUT ATLANTIS AS YOU LOOK FOR THESE FUN ITEMS:

- ☑ Ant
- ☑ Axe
- ☑ Book
- ☑ Chef's hat
- ☑ Chicken
- ☑ Deep-sea diver
- ☑ Deer
- ☑ Elephant
- ☑ Flamingo
- ☑ Frog
- ☑ Guitar
- ☑ Heart
- ☑ Ice-cream cone
- ☑ Kite
- ☑ Lion
- ☑ Mermaid
- ☑ Owl
- ☑ Ox
- ☑ Paintbrush
- ☑ Pelican
- ☑ Periscope
- ☑ Pig
- ☑ Rhinoceros
- ☑ Snail
- ☑ Snake
- ☑ Sock
- ☑ Toucan
- ☑ Turtle
- ☑ Umbrella
- ☑ Unicorn
- ☑ Zebra

Who was Plato?
Some scientists believe that
Atlantis was what island?

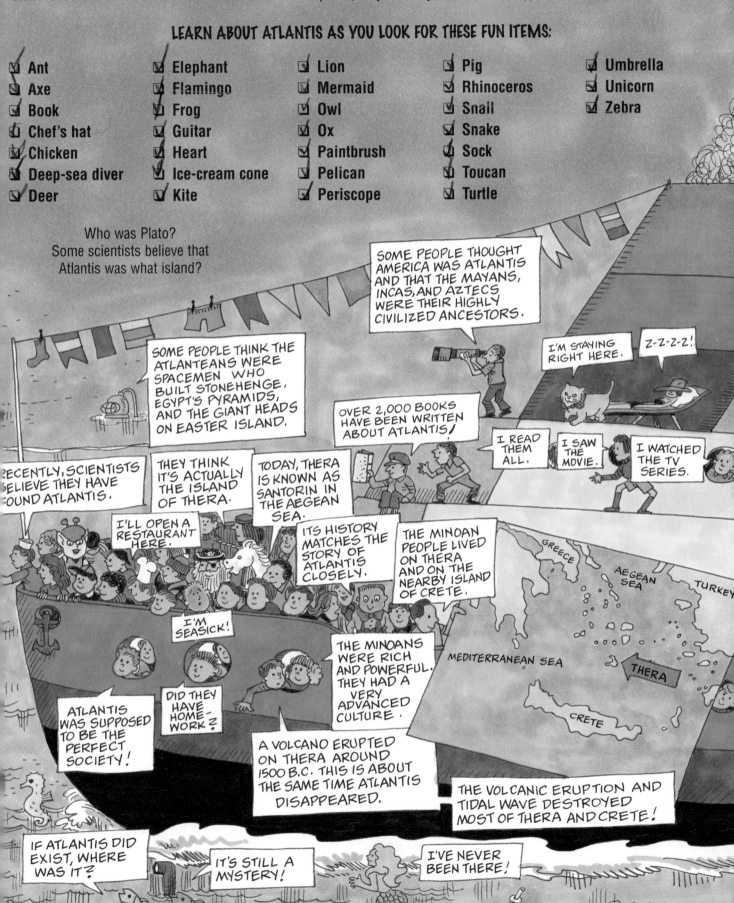

THE TUNGUSKA EXPLOSION

On June 30, 1908, the sky over the icy wilderness of Siberia flashed with a bright streak of light. Suddenly, the earth shook and smoke and fire shot up into the sky, reaching a height of 10 miles. This explosion was so tremendous, it was recorded around the world.

LEARN ABOUT THE TUNGUSKA EXPLOSION AS YOU LOOK FOR THESE FUN ITEMS:

- Arrow
- Bear
- Bell
- Boot
- Camel
- Crayon
- Crown
- Cupcake
- Doll
- Drum
- Elephant
- Fish
- Flashlight
- Flying bat
- Football
- Fork
- Ghost
- Heart
- Hot-air balloon
- Hot dog
- Igloo
- Jack-o'-lantern
- Key
- Kite
- Lips
- Mailbox
- Mask
- Mouse
- Pillow
- Ring
- Sailboat
- Skis
- Snake
- Tin can
- Tire
- Toothbrush
- Top hat
- Tree
- Tulip
- Turtle

What is a meteorite?
When were atomic bombs first produced?

THE MARY CELESTE

People said that the *Mary Celeste* was "born" unlucky. This sailing ship, built in 1861, originally was named the *Amazon*. It went through four captains and numerous catastrophes before it was bought by an American and renamed the *Mary Celeste*. In November 1872, Benjamin Briggs, the new captain and part-owner, along with his family and crew, set sail from New York to Genoa, Italy. However, he, his family, and crew all disappeared en route. The *Mary Celeste* was later found in good condition but, to this day, no one knows what happened on that mysterious voyage.

LEARN ABOUT THE MARY CELESTE AS YOU LOOK FOR THESE FUN ITEMS:

- ❏ Balloons (4)
- ❏ Barrel
- ❏ Broom
- ❏ Cactus
- ❏ Chattering teeth
- ❏ Chef's hat
- ❏ Duck
- ❏ Elephant
- ❏ Fishing pole
- ❏ Flamingo
- ❏ Flowerpot
- ❏ Flying bats (2)
- ❏ Ghost
- ❏ Giraffe
- ❏ Horseshoe
- ❏ Hot dog
- ❏ Humpty Dumpty
- ❏ Mouse
- ❏ Octopus
- ❏ Pelican
- ❏ Periscope
- ❏ Saw
- ❏ Skull and crossbones
- ❏ Sock
- ❏ Surfboard
- ❏ Telescope
- ❏ Turtle
- ❏ Umbrella
- ❏ Whale

What cargo was the *Mary Celeste* carrying? Where was the ship headed when everyone aboard disappeared?

HOW THINGS WORK

COMPUTERS

Rare just a generation ago, computers are now everywhere! As technological know-how improves, these devices keep getting smaller, faster, more reliable, and easier to use.

LEARN ABOUT COMPUTERS AS YOU LOOK FOR THESE FUN ITEMS:

- ❏ Bears (2)
- ❏ Birds (2)
- ❏ Fish (3)
- ❏ Flowers (2)
- ❏ Ghosts (3)
- ❏ Horses (2)
- ❏ Neckerchief
- ❏ Pencils (2)
- ❏ Scarves (2)
- ❏ Sheet of paper
- ❏ Snail
- ❏ Snake
- ❏ Sunglasses (2)
- ❏ Volcanoes (2)

What is another word for modulator/demodulator?
What do *RAM* and *ROM* stand for?

DATA USED BY COMPUTERS ARE STORED ON VARIOUS TYPES OF DEVICES KNOWN AS DISKS. EACH COMPUTER HAS A HARD DISK, WHERE PROGRAMS, FILES, DOCUMENTS, AND OTHER KEY INFORMATION ARE STORED.

DATA STORED ON A COMPUTER'S HARD DRIVE CAN BE COPIED TO REMOVABLE DISKS AND STORED ELSEWHERE. FLOPPY DISKS, CDS, ZIP DISKS, AND DVDs ARE WIDELY USED STORAGE MEDIA.

A MICROCHIP IS A TINY BUT POWERFUL DEVICE THAT CAN HOLD AN IMMENSE AMOUNT OF DATA. AS MICROCHIPS HAVE GOTTEN SMALLER WHILE HOLDING MORE DATA, COMPUTERS HAVE BECOME SMALLER, TOO.

HARDWARE THAT YOU CAN SEE INCLUDES THE SYSTEM UNIT (CPU), MONITOR, KEYBOARD, MOUSE, AND STORAGE DEVICES (SUCH AS FLOPPY DISK, CD-ROM, OR DVD DRIVES).

HARDWARE THAT YOU CAN'T SEE—BECAUSE IT'S INSIDE THE SYSTEM UNIT—INCLUDES THE PROCESSOR AND MEMORY CHIPS.

A PERSONAL COMPUTER (PC) IS ONE THAT IS MEANT TO BE USED BY ONLY ONE PERSON AT A TIME. MOST PEOPLE USE THE WORD *PC* TO DESCRIBE A DESKTOP COMPUTER, BUT LAPTOP AND HAND-HELD COMPUTERS ARE ALSO ONE-PERSON-AT-A-TIME DEVICES.

A KEYBOARD IS USED LIKE A TYPEWRITER. WHEN YOU PRESS A KEY, INFORMATION APPEARS ON THE SCREEN.

PROGRAMS FOR WORD PROCESSING, WEB BROWSING, E-MAIL, PLAYING GAMES, AND MAKING SPREAD-SHEETS OR DATABASES ARE ALL EXAMPLES OF SOFTWARE.

THE SCANNER IS LIKE A CAMERA AND COPY MACHINE ROLLED INTO ONE DEVICE. USING LIGHT, MIRRORS, AND LENSES, IT TURNS AN IMAGE INTO DATA THAT YOUR COMPUTER CAN USE.

DO THEY STILL USE PENCILS?

YOUR COMPUTER MAY HAVE OTHER HARDWARE CALLED *PERIPHERALS*— DEVICES INSTALLED IN OR ATTACHED TO YOUR COMPUTER TO EXPAND WHAT IT CAN DO. COMMON PERIPHERALS INCLUDE MODEMS, PRINTERS, AND SCANNERS.

THE MODEM IS A DEVICE THAT LETS TWO OR MORE COMPUTERS "TALK" TO EACH OTHER. MODEMS SEND SIGNALS THROUGH TELEPHONE, CABLE, OR OTHER COMMUNICATIONS LINES. (MODEM IS SHORT FOR "MOdulator/ DEModulator.")

FOR A COMPUTER TO WORK, YOU NEED BOTH HARDWARE AND SOFTWARE. HARDWARE IS THE EQUIPMENT THAT DOES THE WORK. SOFTWARE IS INFORMATION THAT TELLS THE EQUIPMENT WHAT TO DO AND HOW TO DO IT.

LIGHT BULBS

An electric light bulb is a glass bulb that contains a filament, an inert gas, and electrical contacts. Light is produced when an electrical current passes through the filament. This current heats the filament to a temperature that is high enough to produce light.

Thomas Edison invented the light bulb in 1879.

LEARN HOW LIGHT BULBS WORK AS YOU LOOK FOR THESE FUN ITEMS:

- ❑ Alarm clock
- ❑ Apple
- ❑ Baby's bib
- ❑ Baseball bat
- ❑ Bone
- ❑ Burned-out bulb
- ❑ Candles (2)
- ❑ Clipboard

- ❑ Clown
- ❑ Crayon
- ❑ Elephant
- ❑ Envelope
- ❑ Fish (2)
- ❑ Flowers (2)
- ❑ Football
- ❑ Fork

- ❑ Ghost
- ❑ Heart
- ❑ Helmet
- ❑ Horse's head
- ❑ Horseshoe
- ❑ Hose
- ❑ Jump rope
- ❑ Necktie

- ❑ Paintbrush
- ❑ Paper bag
- ❑ Pencil
- ❑ Pizza box
- ❑ Saw
- ❑ Tepee
- ❑ Used tire
- ❑ Vest

What is a filament made of?
What determines the brightness of a light bulb?

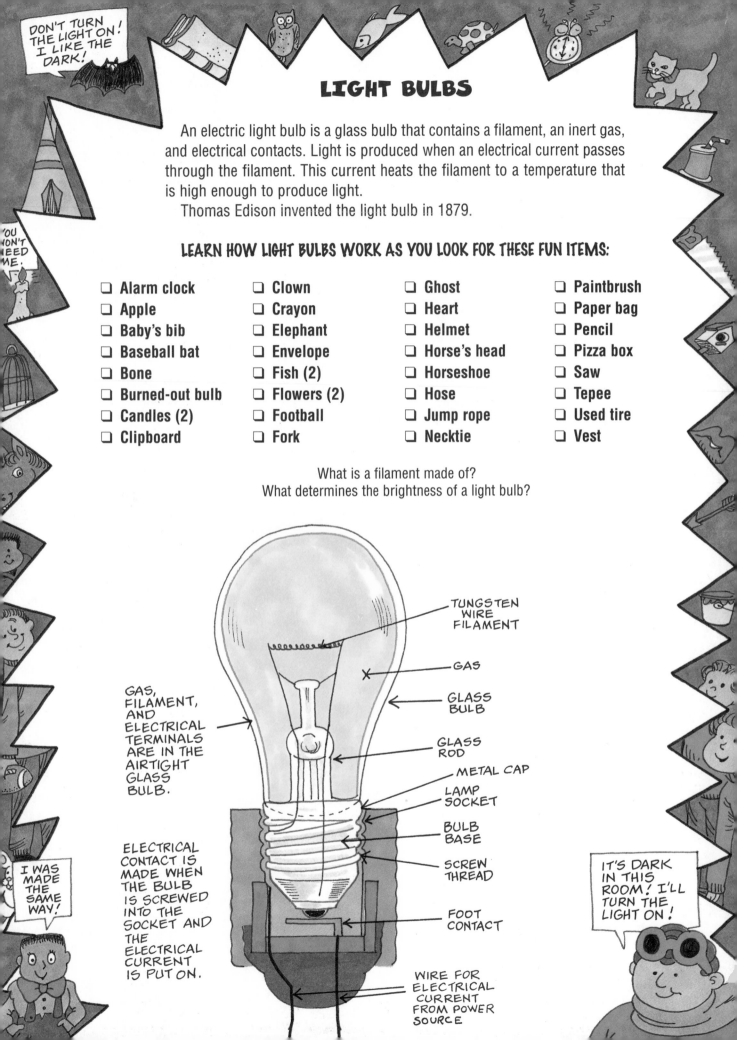

DON'T TURN THE LIGHT ON! I LIKE THE DARK!

YOU DON'T NEED ME.

I WAS MADE THE SAME WAY!

IT'S DARK IN THIS ROOM! I'LL TURN THE LIGHT ON!

TUNGSTEN WIRE FILAMENT

GAS

GLASS BULB

GLASS ROD

METAL CAP

LAMP SOCKET

BULB BASE

SCREW THREAD

FOOT CONTACT

WIRE FOR ELECTRICAL CURRENT FROM POWER SOURCE

GAS, FILAMENT, AND ELECTRICAL TERMINALS ARE IN THE AIRTIGHT GLASS BULB.

ELECTRICAL CONTACT IS MADE WHEN THE BULB IS SCREWED INTO THE SOCKET AND THE ELECTRICAL CURRENT IS PUT ON.

SUBMARINES

A submarine is designed to travel under water. Aided by small moveable fins called *hydroplanes*, it dives and surfaces by filling its ballast tanks with water or air. When the tanks are filled with water, the sub gets heavier and sinks. When compressed air is blown into the tanks, forcing out the water, the sub gets lighter and rises. Power to drive the sub comes from a nuclear reactor or from a combination of diesel and battery-driven engines.

LEARN HOW SUBS WORK AS YOU LOOK FOR THESE FUN ITEMS:

- ❑ Bathtub
- ❑ Book
- ❑ Cactus
- ❑ Clothespins (2)
- ❑ Crown
- ❑ Fish hook
- ❑ Four-leaf clover
- ❑ Frog
- ❑ Ghost
- ❑ Hammer
- ❑ Jellyfish
- ❑ Light bulb
- ❑ Mermaid
- ❑ Mouse
- ❑ Pizza
- ❑ Propellers (3)
- ❑ Sea horse
- ❑ Tuba

What was the *Turtle*? What do hydroplanes do?

HELICOPTERS

Helicopters can fly straight up or down, forward or backward, or sideways; and they can even hover in place. Their mobility allows them to fly into places that airplanes cannot.

The first helicopter to achieve flight was built in France in 1907. It was not reliable, however. In 1939, Igor Sikorsky developed the first successful one, and the modern era of helicopters began.

LEARN HOW HELICOPTERS WORK AS YOU LOOK FOR THESE FUN ITEMS:

- ❑ Balloon
- ❑ Bee
- ❑ Book
- ❑ Bucket
- ❑ Butterfly
- ❑ Cactus
- ❑ Camera
- ❑ Candy cane
- ❑ Canteen

- ❑ Flying bat
- ❑ Frog
- ❑ Heart
- ❑ Jack-o'-lantern
- ❑ Lollipop
- ❑ Medal
- ❑ Mouse
- ❑ Oilcan
- ❑ Owl

- ❑ Paper airplane
- ❑ Penguin
- ❑ Periscope
- ❑ Roller skates
- ❑ Schoolbag
- ❑ Screwdriver
- ❑ Squirrel
- ❑ Tennis racket

How many main rotor blades do most helicopters have?
What gives a helicopter its power?

ORCHESTRAS

An orchestra is not a random gathering of musicians and their instruments. It is a carefully planned group of different types of instruments, with each one having its own part to play in the performance.

LEARN HOW ORCHESTRAS WORK AS YOU LOOK FOR THESE FUN ITEMS:

- ❏ Ball of string
- ❏ Balloon
- ❏ Baseball cap
- ❏ Bird
- ❏ Broom
- ❏ Brush
- ❏ Candle
- ❏ Duck
- ❏ Earring

VIBRAPHONE

TIMPANI

OOPS! WRONG STAGE!

TUBA

FRENCH HORNS

I'M THE MUSICAL SPIRIT.

WHO PUT SOAP IN MY SAXOPHONE?

CLARINE

PIANO

I'M THE KITTEN ON THE PIANO STRINGS.

THE SYMPHONY ORCHESTRA IS THE LARGEST ORCHESTRA.

IT IS MADE UP OF ABOUT 90 MUSICIANS.

FLUTES

STRINGS SECTION

VIOLAS

I PLAY THE RADIO.

THE PRINCIPAL VIOLINIST LEADS ALL THE OTHER MUSICIANS

FIRST VIOLINS

THE SYMPHONY ORCHESTRA IS DIVIDED INTO FOUR MAIN SECTIONS OF INSTRUMENTS. THEY ARE: STRINGS, WOODWINDS, BRASS, AND PERCUSSION.

INSTRUMENTS IN THE STRING SECTION INCLUDE: FIRST AND SECOND VIOLINS, CELLO, VIOLA, DOUBLE BASS, HARP, AND PIANO.

INSTRUMENTS IN THE WOODWIND SECTION INCLUDE: FLUTE, PICCOLO, CLARINET, SAXOPHONE, OBOE, AND BASSOON.

INSTRUMENTS IN THE BRASS SECTION INCLUDE: TRUMPET, TUBA, FRENCH HORN, AND TROMBONE.

INSTRUMENTS IN THE PERCUSSION SECTION INCLUDE: DRUMS, GONG, VIBRAPHONE, AND TIMPANI.

CDs AND DVDs

Whether it's music or movies that you love best, CDs and DVDs make it possible for you to take your favorite tunes and flicks almost anywhere. Those data-packed little plastic disks are a marvel of modern technology.

LEARN ABOUT CDs AND DVDs AS YOU LOOK FOR THESE FUN ITEMS:

- ☐ Apple
- ☐ Balloons (2)
- ☐ Banana peel
- ☐ Boat in a bottle
- ☐ Book
- ☐ Bowling ball
- ☐ Broom
- ☐ Butterfly
- ☐ Candle
- ☐ Clown
- ☐ Crown
- ☐ Donkey
- ☐ Flower
- ☐ Flying saucer
- ☐ Football
- ☐ Hairbrush
- ☐ Jack-o'-lantern
- ☐ Magnifying glass
- ☐ Paper airplane
- ☐ Picnic basket
- ☐ Scarves (2)
- ☐ Scissors
- ☐ Shovel
- ☐ Tent

LABEL
ACRYLIC
ALUMINUM

A CD IS A PRETTY SIMPLE PIECE OF PLASTIC, ABOUT 4/100 OF AN INCH THICK.

IT'S ELEMENTARY!!

Which type of disk has a gold layer? What is a micron?

LET'S DANCE.

THE LONG, SPIRAL TRACK OF BUMPS ON THE CD IS WHERE ALL THE DATA ARE STORED.

THE BUMPS ARE TINY — 0.5 MICRONS WIDE AND 125 NANOMETERS HIGH.

A MICRON IS ONE MILLIONTH OF A METER.

A NANOMETER IS ONE BILLIONTH OF A METER.

THE MICROSCOPIC BUMPS ARE THEN COVERED WITH A LAYER OF ALUMINUM, THEN A LAYER OF ACRYLIC.

THE PLASTIC IS IMPRESSED WITH ONE LONG SPIRAL OF MICROSCOPIC BUMPS.

THE CD LABEL IS PRINTED ON THE ACRYLIC LAYER.

A CD PLAYER FOCUSES A LASER ON THE ALUMINUM LAYER OF THE CD.

AS THE LASER MOVES OVER THE BUMPS, IT GETS REFLECTED.

A SENSOR IN THE CD PLAYER DETECTS THE CHANGES IN REFLECTION AND READS THAT INFORMATION, WHICH COMES ACROSS TO YOU AS MUSIC OR DATA ON YOUR COMPUTER.

LOWER THAT MUSIC!

IF THE DATA TRACK WAS LIFTED OFF A CD AND LAID IN A STRAIGHT LINE, IT WOULD BE 0.5 MICRONS WIDE AND 3.5 MILES LONG.

THE HUMAN HEART

A heart is a muscular pump that circulates blood through the blood vessels. The blood carries nourishment and oxygen to every part of the body. In one year, the human heart pumps about 650,000 gallons of blood, enough to fill 50 swimming pools!

LEARN HOW THE HUMAN HEART WORKS AS YOU LOOK FOR THESE FUN ITEMS:

- ☐ Ball
- ☐ Banana peel
- ☐ Barrel
- ☐ Baseball hat
- ☐ Book
- ☐ Candy cane
- ☐ Chicken
- ☐ Dracula
- ☐ Drum
- ☐ Duck
- ☐ Flower
- ☐ Joggers (2)
- ☐ Lion
- ☐ Microscope
- ☐ Mouse
- ☐ Mustache
- ☐ Owl
- ☐ Pillow
- ☐ Propeller
- ☐ Roller skates
- ☐ Saw
- ☐ Singer
- ☐ Skateboard
- ☐ Stars (2)
- ☐ Top hat
- ☐ TV set
- ☐ Umbrella
- ☐ Worm

What are the heart's chambers called?

Approximately how long does it take for the blood to travel throughout the body?

EXERCISE IS GOOD FOR YOUR HEALTH.

I HAVE A HEART.

I'M GOING TO OZ TO GET A HEART.

A DROP OF BLOOD THE SIZE OF THE HEAD OF A PIN HAS ABOUT FIVE MILLION CELLS.

CELLS!

I FEEL LIKE A BLOODHOUND.

THE HUMAN HEART IS PROTECTED BY THE RIB CAGE IN OUR BODY.

AN ADULT'S HEART IS ABOUT THE SIZE OF A CLENCHED FIST.

IT WEIGHS ABOUT NINE OUNCES.

HEART

RIB CAGE

I LOST MY HEART IN SAN FRANCISCO!

YOU LOST YOUR VOICE THERE, TOO!!

IT HAS A NICE BEAT.

ALIENS HAVE HEARTS, TOO.

IT TAKES ABOUT ONE MINUTE FOR THE BLOOD TO COMPLETE ITS JOURNEY THROUGH THE BODY.

THE HEARTBEAT HAS TWO STAGES. THE ATRIUMS CONTRACT FIRST, FOLLOWED BY THE VENTRICLES. THESE STAGES ARE WHAT CAUSES THE WELL-KNOWN "THUMP-THUMP" SOUND.

THE HEARTBEAT IS AUTOMATICALLY CONTROLLED BY THE NERVOUS SYSTEM. IN-BETWEEN BEATS, THE HEART RESTS.

EACH CHAMBER HAS VALVES THAT CONTROL THE DIRECTION OF BLOOD FLOW THROUGH THE HEART. THEY OPEN AND CLOSE AS THE HEART EXPANDS AND CONTRACTS.

I HAVE A HEART.

I DIDN'T KNOW THAT!

THAT'S FAST!

I KNOW IT NOW!

AN ADULT'S AVERAGE HEARTBEAT IS 60 TO 70 TIMES A MINUTE.

OUR BODY CONTAINS ABOUT TEN AND ONE-HALF PINTS OF BLOOD.

DID SOMEONE SAY BLOOD?

THE BLOOD ENTERS THE ATRIA IN THE UPPER CHAMBERS.

THE BLOOD FLOWS THROUGH TO THE VENTRICLES IN THE LOWER CHAMBERS.

THE VENTRICLES RELAX AND FILL WITH BLOOD.

THE VENTRICLES CONTRACT TO PUMP BLOOD INTO THE ARTERIES.

SOLAR ENERGY

Solar energy is power produced by the sun. It can be used to heat and purify water, give power to engines, and produce electricity. A person would have to burn 550 billion tons of coal in order to equal the amount of solar energy received by Earth in one day!

LEARN HOW SOLAR ENERGY WORKS AS YOU LOOK FOR THESE FUN ITEMS:

- ❑ Apple
- ❑ Arrow
- ❑ Baseball
- ❑ Basketball hoop
- ❑ Bone
- ❑ Bowling ball
- ❑ Brush
- ❑ Buckets (2)
- ❑ Doghouse
- ❑ Duck
- ❑ Earmuffs
- ❑ Fire hydrant
- ❑ Flower
- ❑ Football
- ❑ Hammer
- ❑ Heart
- ❑ Helmet
- ❑ Kite
- ❑ Mailbox
- ❑ Newspaper
- ❑ Rabbit
- ❑ Screwdriver
- ❑ Star
- ❑ Turtle
- ❑ Umbrella
- ❑ Umpire
- ❑ Watering can
- ❑ Worm

What is solar power most commonly used for?
Why are the insides of solar panels painted black?

WHICH MOVES FASTER, HEAT OR COLD?

HEAT, BECAUSE YOU CAN CATCH COLD.

ONE OF THE MOST COMMON USES OF SOLAR POWER IS TO HEAT HOUSES.

SOLAR PANELS ARE USED TO COLLECT THE SUN'S RAYS AND TURN THEM INTO HEAT.

THEY WORK LIKE A GREENHOUSE. GLASS SHEETS COVER THE PANELS, TRAPPING THE SUN'S RAYS BY ALLOWING THEM IN, BUT NOT OUT!

ALUMINUM FOIL REFLECTS HEAT RAYS.

OOPS!

I MIGHT BE OUT OF A JOB.

I FLY SOUTH FOR THE WINTER.

THE INSIDES OF THE PANELS ARE PAINTED BLACK TO ABSORB AS MUCH HEAT AS POSSIBLE.

SOLAR POWER IS NON-POLLUTING

COOL WATER IS PUMPED THROUGH COPPER TUBING IN THE PANELS. THE COPPER ABSORBS THE HEAT AND PASSES IT TO THE WATER.

HEATED WATER FLOWS TO A HOT WATER TANK.

THE HOT WATER TANK IS INSULATED IN ORDER TO KEEP THE WATER HOT!

A WATER PUMP IS USED TO CIRCULATE THE WATER THROUGH THE SOLAR PANELS.

WINDOWS ARE A PANE!

DO YOU HAVE A CARROT?

AIRPLANES

Airplanes are fascinating pieces of machinery that soar through the air. Whether passenger, private, or military, they all operate under the same aerodynamic principles.

The first power-driven flight was made by the Wright brothers at Kitty Hawk, North Carolina, in 1903.

LEARN HOW AIRPLANES WORK AS YOU LOOK FOR THESE FUN ITEMS:

- ❑ "X-1"
- ❑ Acrobat
- ❑ Banana
- ❑ Bowling ball
- ❑ Broom
- ❑ Elephant
- ❑ Fishing pole
- ❑ Flowers (3)
- ❑ Flying carpet
- ❑ Flying horse
- ❑ Flying saucer
- ❑ Football
- ❑ Ghost
- ❑ Glider
- ❑ Hamburger
- ❑ Hang glider
- ❑ Kite
- ❑ Mouse
- ❑ Paper airplane
- ❑ Pencil
- ❑ Pinwheel
- ❑ Pizza
- ❑ Sailboat
- ❑ Seaplane
- ❑ Sled
- ❑ Stars (2)
- ❑ Superheroes (2)
- ❑ Surfboard
- ❑ Umbrella
- ❑ Yo-yo

What provides an airplane's lift?
What kind of engine "pulls" the airplane through the air?

FLAPS ON BOTH WINGS MOVE TO STEER PLANE.

IN 1891, OTTO LILIENTHAL, A GERMAN, BECAME THE FIRST PERSON TO FLY SUCCESSFULLY IN A HANG-GLIDER.

TAILFIN

RUDDER

I'M HITCHING A RIDE.

PUNT!

USUALLY, THE GREATER THE WEIGHT OF THE AIRPLANE THE LARGER THE WINGS WILL BE.

TAIL FLAPS MOVE TO STEER AIRPLANE

I'M NOT A FLYING SAUCER!

747

POST NO BILLS

WHERE'S THE SURF?

I DON'T HAVE AN ENGINE.

IT'S EASY TO FLY.

I HAVE NO FUEL PROBLEM.

STABILIZER

AN AIRPLANE'S LIFT IS PROVIDED BY THE WINGS.

SEAPLANES CAN LAND ON THE WATER.

A WING IS ROUNDED ON TOP AND FLAT ON THE BOTTOM.

THE ENGINE PROVIDES THE THRUST, OR FORCE, NECESSARY FOR TAKEOFF. WHILE AIRBORNE, ITS POWER MAINTAINS AND CHANGES THE AIRPLANE'S SPEED.

LOWER AIR PRESSURE

WING

LIFT

TURBOJET ENGINE

COMBUSTION CHAMBER

IGNITER

FUEL NOZZLE

EXHAUST GASES

AIR INTAKE

JET NOZZLE

COMPRESSOR

HELLO EARTHLINGS!

I DIDN'T KNOW THAT!

THE AIR FLOWING OVER THE ROUNDED PART TRAVELS A GREATER DISTANCE THAN THE AIR FLOWING PAST THE FLAT PART. THE AIR ABOVE MOVES FASTER AND LOSES PRESSURE AS IT "STRETCHES OUT" GOING OVER THE ROUNDED SECTION.

LASERS

A laser is a device that intensifies or increases light. It produces a thin beam of light, stronger than sunlight, that can burn a hole through diamond or steel.

The first operational laser was built in 1960.

LEARN HOW LASERS WORK AS YOU LOOK FOR THESE FUN ITEMS:

- ☐ Apple
- ☐ Book
- ☐ Cheerleader
- ☐ Chicken
- ☐ Clock
- ☐ Drinking straw
- ☐ Drum

- ☐ Electrodes (2)
- ☐ Envelope
- ☐ Fish tank
- ☐ Flamingo
- ☐ Football
- ☐ Frog
- ☐ Globe

- ☐ Hot dog
- ☐ Little Red Riding Hood
- ☐ Necktie
- ☐ Orangutan
- ☐ Painted egg
- ☐ Paper airplane
- ☐ Parrot

- ☐ Rabbit
- ☐ Roller skates
- ☐ Stapler
- ☐ Stethoscope
- ☐ Thermometer
- ☐ Umbrella
- ☐ Vase

Name two types of lasers.
What are some of the uses of laser beams?

MAGNETS AND MAGNETISM

A magnet is often thought of as a toy that can pull or pick up metal objects. However, the invisible force of magnetism is used in a wide variety of modern devices.

Magnetite, an iron ore with magnetic properties, was used as a compass by early sailors to navigate.

LEARN HOW MAGNETS AND MAGNETISM WORK AS YOU LOOK FOR THESE FUN ITEMS:

- ❏ Bent nail
- ❏ Cactus
- ❏ Clown
- ❏ Compasses (2)
- ❏ Dart
- ❏ Duck
- ❏ Flower
- ❏ Football player
- ❏ Hard hats (2)
- ❏ Hooks (2)
- ❏ Hot dog
- ❏ Ice-cream cone
- ❏ Kangaroo
- ❏ Key
- ❏ Lion
- ❏ Mermaid
- ❏ Mouse
- ❏ Periscope
- ❏ Pillow
- ❏ Ringmaster
- ❏ Rocking chair
- ❏ Safety pin
- ❏ Sewing needle
- ❏ Shovel
- ❏ Snake
- ❏ Spoon
- ❏ Tin Man
- ❏ TV antenna

When is a metal magnetized?
Where are Earth's two magnetic poles?

Sports

BASKETBALL

Basketball is played in more than 200 countries around the world. To play, all you need are a ball, a basket or hoop, and a level surface. Basketball can be played indoors or out, alone or with others, at night or by day, 365 days a year!

LEARN ABOUT BASKETBALL AS YOU LOOK FOR THESE FUN ITEMS:

- ☐ Balloons (5)
- ☐ Banana peel
- ☐ Bowling ball
- ☐ Boxing glove
- ☐ Bucket
- ☐ Cane
- ☐ Clock
- ☐ Crown
- ☐ Football
- ☐ Graduate
- ☐ Ice skate
- ☐ Kite
- ☐ Lost shoe
- ☐ Mermaid
- ☐ Monkey
- ☐ Mouse
- ☐ Pencil
- ☐ Piggy bank
- ☐ Scarecrow
- ☐ Skateboard
- ☐ Soccer ball
- ☐ Top hat
- ☐ Turtle

Name the NBA's career scoring leader.

PROFESSIONAL TEAMS PLAY FOUR 12-MINUTE QUARTERS, OR 48 MINUTES.

TIMER

THE MOST POINTS IN NBA HISTORY WERE SCORED BY KAREEM ABDUL-JABBAR—38,387!

I'M NOT ON THE TEAM.

I'M IN THE WRONG GAME.

I SCORED 3 POINTS ALL SEASON.

BLOCK THE SHOT!

BASKETS ARE TEN FEET ABOVE THE GROUND AND 18 INCHES IN DIAMETER.

PRO BACKBOARDS ARE 72 INCHES WIDE AND 42 INCHES HIGH.

THE NET SLOWS THE BALL DOWN AS IT GOES THROUGH THE BASKET.

CENTER LINE

JOHN STOCKTON HAD 1,164 ASSISTS IN ONE SEASON.

I'M LOST.

BASKETBALL BECAME AN OLYMPIC SPORT IN 1936.

WILT CHAMBERLAIN HAD 55 REBOUNDS IN ONE GAME!

EACH TEAM USES TWO GUARDS, TWO FORWARDS, AND ONE CENTER.

PRO PLAYERS MUST SHOOT THE BALL WITHIN 24 SECONDS— COLLEGE PLAYERS WITHIN 35 SECONDS.

THE WOMEN'S NATIONAL BASKETBALL ASSOCIATION (WNBA) BEGAN PLAY IN 1997.

HAKEEM OLAJUWAN BLOCKED MORE THAN 3,500 SHOTS IN HIS NBA CAREER.

WILT CHAMBERLAIN PLAYED 1,945 GAMES (HIS ENTIRE CAREER) WITHOUT FOULING OUT!

I SURE DID.

COULD SHE SLAM-DUNK?

PEARL MOORE SCORED 4,061 POINTS FOR FRANCIS MARION COLLEGE — THE MOST BY A WOMAN IN A COLLEGE CAREER!

I DIDN'T KNOW THAT!

I KNOW IT NOW!

GYMNASTICS

In gymnastics, acrobatic exercises are performed on various pieces of equipment. Gymnastics helps develop balance, agility, and strength. During the Olympics of 1972 and 1976, the emergence of two superstars—Olga Korbut and Nadia Comaneci—helped give gymnastics worldwide popularity.

LEARN ABOUT GYMNASTICS AS YOU LOOK FOR THESE FUN ITEMS:

- ❏ Banana peel
- ❏ Bear
- ❏ Broom
- ❏ Crutch
- ❏ Duck
- ❏ Elephant
- ❏ Juggler
- ❏ Kangaroo
- ❏ Mail carrier
- ❏ Pillow
- ❏ Scarecrow
- ❏ Snowman
- ❏ Star
- ❏ Telescope
- ❏ TV camera
- ❏ Unicorn
- ❏ Water skier

Who was the first Olympic gymnast to earn a perfect 10? Name the eight events in which men compete.

NASCAR RACING

NASCAR racing is fast becoming one of the most popular spectator sports in the U.S. With more than 7 million fans a year attending at NASCAR events, not all of the roars you'll hear at the track are coming from the car engines!

LEARN ABOUT NASCAR RACING AS YOU LOOK FOR THESE FUN ITEMS:

- ❑ Astronaut
- ❑ Balloon
- ❑ Birds (2)
- ❑ Bone
- ❑ Elephant
- ❑ Fish
- ❑ Flowers
- ❑ Heart
- ❑ Jockey
- ❑ Kangaroo
- ❑ Kite
- ❑ Pirate
- ❑ Rabbit
- ❑ Sailboat
- ❑ Scuba diver
- ❑ Oilcan
- ❑ Table
- ❑ Tepee
- ❑ Turtle

How long is the Daytona International Speedway?
Who won the first race there?

FOOTBALL

On November 6, 1869, the universities of Rutgers and Princeton met in New Brunswick, New Jersey, in the first college football game. Rutgers won it, 6–4.

The early games were a modified version of soccer and rugby. Football pioneers, such as Walter Camp, instituted 11-man teams, downs and yards to go, a smaller field, the line of scrimmage, and a new system of scoring.

OFFENSE:
C – CENTER
G – GUARD
WR – WIDE RECEIVER
T – TACKLE
TE – TIGHT END
QB – QUARTERBACK
B – BACK
DEFENSE:
DT – DEFENSIVE TACKLE
DE – DEFENSIVE END
LB – LINEBACKER
DB – DEFENSIVE BACK
FS – FREE SAFETY
SS – STRONG SAFETY
NT – NOSE TACKLE

LEARN ABOUT FOOTBALL AS YOU LOOK FOR THESE FUN ITEMS:

- ☐ Air pump
- ☐ Arrow
- ☐ Birds (3)
- ☐ Blimp
- ☐ Bowling pin
- ☐ Candy cane
- ☐ Clipboard
- ☐ Fish
- ☐ Flying bat
- ☐ Ghost
- ☐ Hamburger
- ☐ Heart
- ☐ Horseshoe
- ☐ Hot dog
- ☐ Locker
- ☐ Lost sneaker
- ☐ Mask
- ☐ Mummy
- ☐ Pencil
- ☐ Snowman
- ☐ Straw
- ☐ Telescope
- ☐ Trophy
- ☐ Turtle
- ☐ Water bucket
- ☐ Whistle
- ☐ Worm

What is a punt?
What is a player's shirt called?

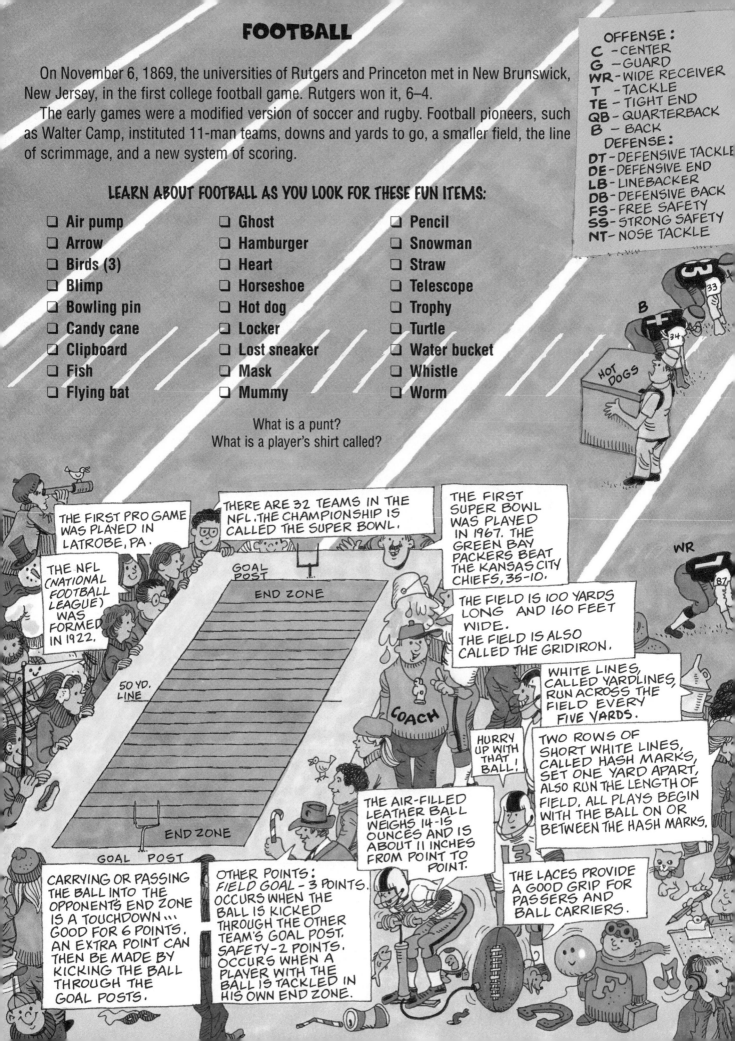

THE FIRST PRO GAME WAS PLAYED IN LATROBE, PA.

THE NFL (NATIONAL FOOTBALL LEAGUE) WAS FORMED IN 1922.

THERE ARE 32 TEAMS IN THE NFL. THE CHAMPIONSHIP IS CALLED THE SUPER BOWL.

THE FIRST SUPER BOWL WAS PLAYED IN 1967. THE GREEN BAY PACKERS BEAT THE KANSAS CITY CHIEFS, 35-10.

THE FIELD IS 100 YARDS LONG AND 160 FEET WIDE.
THE FIELD IS ALSO CALLED THE GRIDIRON.

WHITE LINES, CALLED YARDLINES, RUN ACROSS THE FIELD EVERY FIVE YARDS.

HURRY UP WITH THAT BALL!

TWO ROWS OF SHORT WHITE LINES, CALLED HASH MARKS, SET ONE YARD APART, ALSO RUN THE LENGTH OF FIELD. ALL PLAYS BEGIN WITH THE BALL ON OR BETWEEN THE HASH MARKS.

GOAL POST

END ZONE

50 YD. LINE

COACH

END ZONE

GOAL POST

THE AIR-FILLED LEATHER BALL WEIGHS 14-15 OUNCES AND IS ABOUT 11 INCHES FROM POINT TO POINT.

THE LACES PROVIDE A GOOD GRIP FOR PASSERS AND BALL CARRIERS.

CARRYING OR PASSING THE BALL INTO THE OPPONENT'S END ZONE IS A TOUCHDOWN ... GOOD FOR 6 POINTS. AN EXTRA POINT CAN THEN BE MADE BY KICKING THE BALL THROUGH THE GOAL POSTS.

OTHER POINTS: FIELD GOAL – 3 POINTS. OCCURS WHEN THE BALL IS KICKED THROUGH THE OTHER TEAM'S GOAL POST. SAFETY – 2 POINTS. OCCURS WHEN A PLAYER WITH THE BALL IS TACKLED IN HIS OWN END ZONE.

HOT DOGS

B

WR

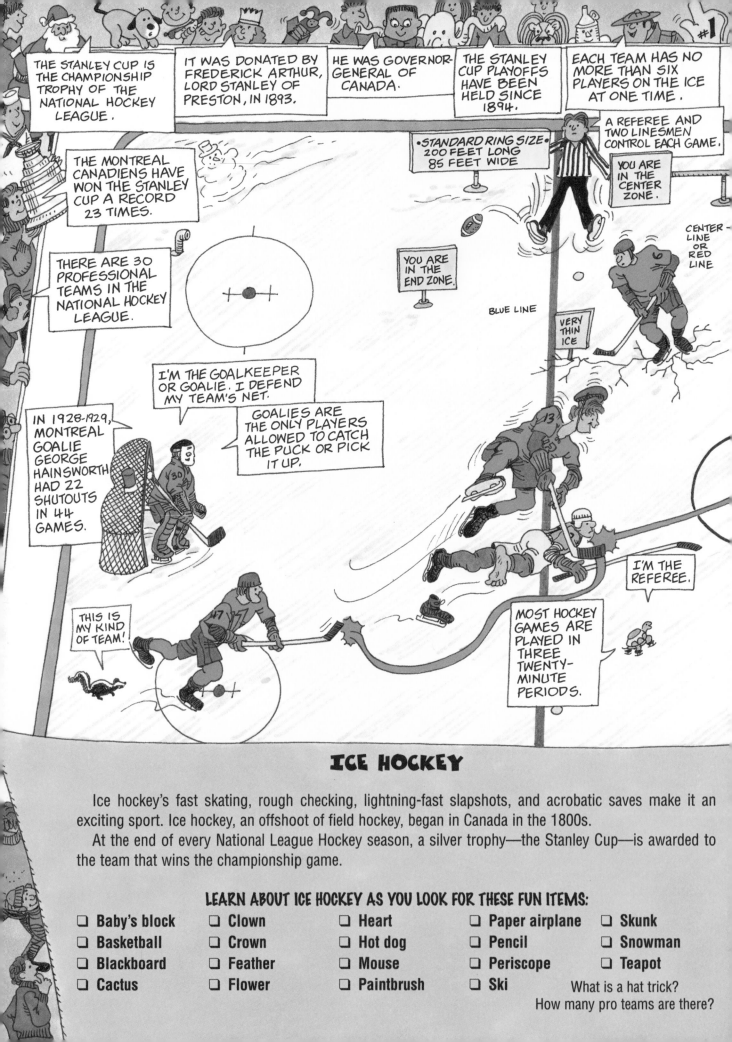

THE STANLEY CUP IS THE CHAMPIONSHIP TROPHY OF THE NATIONAL HOCKEY LEAGUE.

IT WAS DONATED BY FREDERICK ARTHUR, LORD STANLEY OF PRESTON, IN 1893.

HE WAS GOVERNOR-GENERAL OF CANADA.

THE STANLEY CUP PLAYOFFS HAVE BEEN HELD SINCE 1894.

EACH TEAM HAS NO MORE THAN SIX PLAYERS ON THE ICE AT ONE TIME.

THE MONTREAL CANADIENS HAVE WON THE STANLEY CUP A RECORD 23 TIMES.

•STANDARD RING SIZE• 200 FEET LONG 85 FEET WIDE

A REFEREE AND TWO LINESMEN CONTROL EACH GAME.

YOU ARE IN THE CENTER ZONE.

THERE ARE 30 PROFESSIONAL TEAMS IN THE NATIONAL HOCKEY LEAGUE.

YOU ARE IN THE END ZONE.

BLUE LINE

CENTER LINE OR RED LINE

VERY THIN ICE

I'M THE GOALKEEPER OR GOALIE. I DEFEND MY TEAM'S NET.

GOALIES ARE THE ONLY PLAYERS ALLOWED TO CATCH THE PUCK OR PICK IT UP.

IN 1928-1929, MONTREAL GOALIE GEORGE HAINSWORTH HAD 22 SHUTOUTS IN 44 GAMES.

THIS IS MY KIND OF TEAM!

I'M THE REFEREE.

MOST HOCKEY GAMES ARE PLAYED IN THREE TWENTY-MINUTE PERIODS.

ICE HOCKEY

Ice hockey's fast skating, rough checking, lightning-fast slapshots, and acrobatic saves make it an exciting sport. Ice hockey, an offshoot of field hockey, began in Canada in the 1800s.

At the end of every National League Hockey season, a silver trophy—the Stanley Cup—is awarded to the team that wins the championship game.

LEARN ABOUT ICE HOCKEY AS YOU LOOK FOR THESE FUN ITEMS:

❑ Baby's block	❑ Clown	❑ Heart	❑ Paper airplane	❑ Skunk
❑ Basketball	❑ Crown	❑ Hot dog	❑ Pencil	❑ Snowman
❑ Blackboard	❑ Feather	❑ Mouse	❑ Periscope	❑ Teapot
❑ Cactus	❑ Flower	❑ Paintbrush	❑ Ski	

What is a hat trick?
How many pro teams are there?

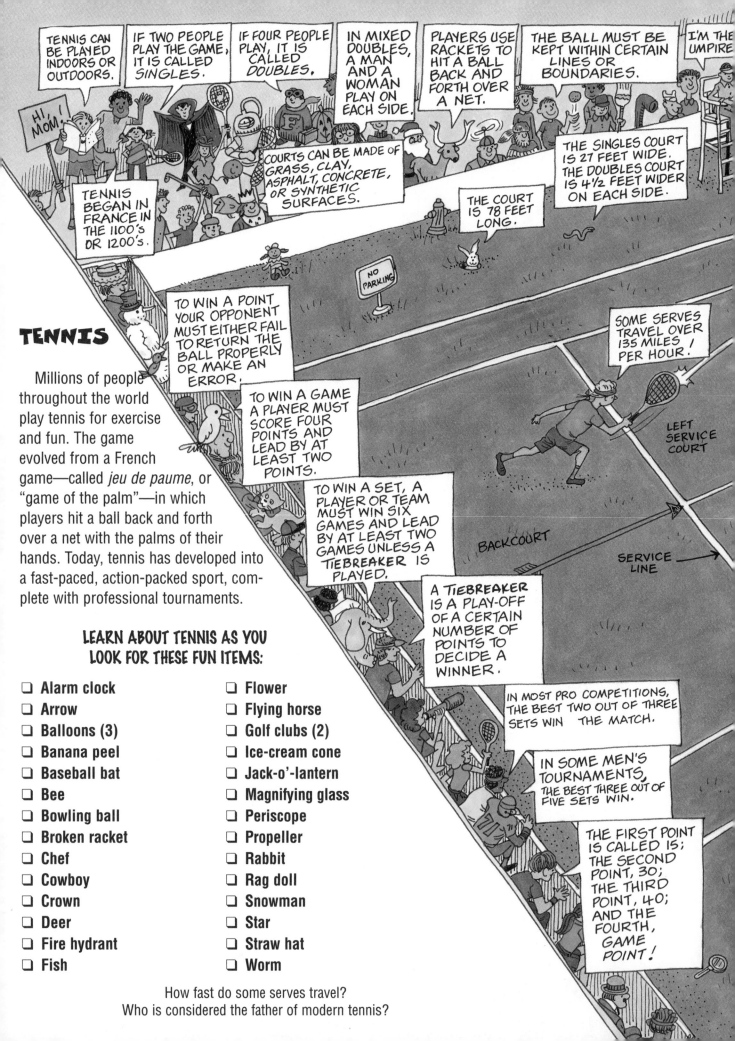

TENNIS

Millions of people throughout the world play tennis for exercise and fun. The game evolved from a French game—called *jeu de paume*, or "game of the palm"—in which players hit a ball back and forth over a net with the palms of their hands. Today, tennis has developed into a fast-paced, action-packed sport, complete with professional tournaments.

LEARN ABOUT TENNIS AS YOU LOOK FOR THESE FUN ITEMS:

- Alarm clock
- Arrow
- Balloons (3)
- Banana peel
- Baseball bat
- Bee
- Bowling ball
- Broken racket
- Chef
- Cowboy
- Crown
- Deer
- Fire hydrant
- Fish
- Flower
- Flying horse
- Golf clubs (2)
- Ice-cream cone
- Jack-o'-lantern
- Magnifying glass
- Periscope
- Propeller
- Rabbit
- Rag doll
- Snowman
- Star
- Straw hat
- Worm

How fast do some serves travel?
Who is considered the father of modern tennis?

MARTIAL ARTS

The martial arts are more than a method of combat. They are important as a means of developing one's physical, spiritual, and mental well-being.

Centuries ago, Buddhist monks roamed throughout Asia, spreading their philosophy and knowledge of the martial arts. Each culture modified this philosophy to suit its needs, thus developing new martial arts techniques.

LEARN ABOUT MARTIAL ARTS AS YOU LOOK FOR THESE FUN ITEMS:

- ❑ Anchor
- ❑ Artist
- ❑ Banana peel
- ❑ Bird
- ❑ Black-belt ghost
- ❑ Bone
- ❑ Book
- ❑ Boxer
- ❑ Carrot
- ❑ Cat
- ❑ Chef's hat
- ❑ Clown
- ❑ Crown
- ❑ Football
- ❑ Jack-o'-lantern
- ❑ Karate rat
- ❑ Lost boot
- ❑ Lost glove
- ❑ Lost mitten
- ❑ Magnet
- ❑ Mummy
- ❑ Piggy bank
- ❑ Saw
- ❑ Scarecrow
- ❑ Skateboard
- ❑ Snake
- ❑ Speaker
- ❑ Stopwatch
- ❑ Wizard
- ❑ Yo-yo

What is tae kwon do? How do karate students toughen their hands and feet?

KARATE IS A FORM OF UNARMED COMBAT IN WHICH A PERSON KICKS OR STRIKES WITH HANDS, ELBOWS, FEET, OR KNEES.

THERE ARE FOUR MAJOR TYPES OF KARATE — CHINESE, JAPANESE, KOREAN, AND OKINAWAN.

THE JAPANESE WORD FOR KARATE MEANS EMPTY HAND TAKEN FROM "KARA," EMPTY, AND "TE," HAND.

TAE KWON DO IS THE KOREAN ART OF SELF-DEFENSE. IT EMPHASIZES KICKING. IT MEANS "FOOT-HAND ART."

TAE KWON DO COMBINES PHYSICAL AND MENTAL DISCIPLINE WITH A DEEP PHILOSOPHY.

IT'S AN OLYMPIC SPORT AND HAS BEEN PRACTICED FOR OVER 2,000 YEARS.

I'M KARATE RAT.

FOUR JUDGES— ONE SEATED AT EACH CORNER

- •ARBITRATOR
- •TIMEKEEPER
- •RECORDKEEPER
- •ADMINISTRATOR

STARTING LINE

REFEREE

STARTING LINE

STUDENTS TOUGHEN THEIR HANDS AND FEET BY POUNDING PADDED BOARDS.

CHINESE KARATE IS CALLED KUNG FU.

IT USES FLOWING, CIRCULAR MOTIONS.

THE BELT DENOTES THE WEARER'S RANK.

BEGINNERS WEAR WHITE.

EXPERTS WEAR BLACK.

OTHER COLORS DENOTE INTERMEDIATE RANKS.

THE UNIFORM IS CALLED GI.

MY PANTS SPLIT!

I HAVE A BLACK BELT.

TRACK AND FIELD

Track and field is a sport in which men and women compete in athletic events that feature running, throwing, and jumping. Track events consist of a series of races over various distances, ranging from 60 meters (65.6 yards) to a marathon. Field events measure an athlete's ability to throw or jump.

LEARN ABOUT TRACK AND FIELD AS YOU LOOK FOR THESE FUN ITEMS:

- ☐ Balloon
- ☐ Bee
- ☐ Birdcage
- ☐ Chef's hat
- ☐ Count Dracula
- ☐ Duck
- ☐ Elephant
- ☐ Fish
- ☐ Flying bat
- ☐ Football player
- ☐ Helicopter
- ☐ Ice-cream cone
- ☐ Mummy
- ☐ Ostrich
- ☐ Painted egg
- ☐ Periscope
- ☐ Pig
- ☐ Pizza deliveryman
- ☐ Rabbit
- ☐ Roller skater
- ☐ Surfboard
- ☐ Tuba
- ☐ Turtle
- ☐ Umbrella

How long is a marathon?
Name the four throwing events.

TRACK EVENTS CONSIST OF RACES OVER VARIOUS DISTANCES.

FIELD EVENTS TEST THE ATHLETE'S SKILL AT JUMPING AND THROWING.

ALL RACES UP TO 400 METERS OR 440 YARDS ARE CALLED SPRINTS OR DASHES.

RAYMOND CLARENCE EWRY, OF THE U.S., WON A TOTAL OF 10 GOLD MEDALS IN THE 1900, 1904, 1906, AND 1908 OLYMPICS.

IN 1988, FLORENCE JOYNER GRIFFITH SET THE WOMEN'S RECORD FOR THE 100-METER DASH: 10.49 SECONDS.

TV COVERAGE

IN 1954, ROGER BANNISTER OF GREAT BRITAIN WAS THE FIRST RUNNER TO BREAK THE 4-MINUTE MILE RECORD.

TRACK AND FIELD IS HELD OUTDOORS AND INDOORS. SEPARATE RECORDS ARE KEPT FOR EACH.

PAAVO NURMI OF FINLAND WON FOUR OLYMPIC GOLD MEDALS IN 1924. HE FINISHED HIS CAREER WITH 12 MEDALS (NINE GOLD AND THREE SILVER).

I'M A TRACK AND FIELD STAR.

JESSE OWENS SET SIX WORLD RECORDS IN 45 MINUTES, IN 1935. THE EVENTS WERE: 100-YARD DASH, LONG JUMP, 200-METER DASH, 220-YARD AND 200-METER LOW HURDLES.

NO. 1

DISCUS AREA

THE DECATHLON IS MADE UP OF 10 EVENTS. THEY ARE ...

SHOT PUT AREA

OVAL TRACK

HIGH-JUMP AREA

SAND PIT

FOAM RUBBER PIT

LONG-JUMP AREA

JAVELIN AREA

THE ATHLETES RACE ON AN OVAL TRACK.

MOST OUTDOOR TRACKS ARE ¼ MILE OR 400 METERS LONG.

EXTREME SPORTS

What's more fun than taking action to the edge? "Nothing!" say extreme-sports fans.

LEARN ABOUT BMX AS YOU LOOK FOR THESE FUN ITEMS:

- ❑ Brush
- ❑ Flower
- ❑ Football
- ❑ Key
- ❑ Paintbrush
- ❑ Snail
- ❑ Star
- ❑ Worms (2)

LEARN ABOUT SNOWBOARDING AS YOU LOOK FOR THESE FUN ITEMS:

- ❑ Baseball cap
- ❑ Birds (2)
- ❑ Cactus
- ❑ Heart
- ❑ Lost cap
- ❑ Rabbit
- ❑ Sled
- ❑ Star
- ❑ Sunglasses

LEARN ABOUT SKATEBOARDING AS YOU LOOK FOR THESE FUN ITEMS:

- ❑ Balloons
- ❑ Elephant
- ❑ Half moon
- ❑ Kite
- ❑ Lightning bolts (2)
- ❑ Stars (3)
- ❑ Top hat

What does *BMX* stand for?
Who invented the snowboard?
What is an Ollie?

FAMOUS PEOPLE
AND PLACES

WALT DISNEY WORLD

Walt Disney World is the fulfillment of Walt Disney's dream. He wanted to create the ultimate amusement park, which adults and children could enjoy together. Today, Walt Disney World in Florida is the most popular man-made attraction in the world, visited by thousands of people each day.

LEARN ABOUT WALT DISNEY WORLD AS YOU LOOK FOR THESE FUN ITEMS:

- ❑ Arrow
- ❑ Balloon
- ❑ Cake
- ❑ Chef's hat
- ❑ Clown
- ❑ Elephants (2)
- ❑ Fish
- ❑ Football
- ❑ Ghost
- ❑ Hearts (3)
- ❑ Horse
- ❑ Ice-cream cone
- ❑ Kite
- ❑ Ladder
- ❑ Magnifying glass
- ❑ Penguin
- ❑ Snowman
- ❑ TV set

Who starred in *Steamboat Willie*?
On what day is Walt Disney World busiest?

SACAGAWEA

Sacagawea *(SAK-uh-juh-WEE-uh)* was born among the Shoshone *(shoh-SHOH-nee)* Indians. As a young girl, she was captured by an enemy tribe, then sold as a slave to a French-Canadian trader, who later married her. Sacagawea and her husband both joined the expedition led by Meriwether Lewis and William Clark in 1804-1805. Sacagawea served as interpreter and guide as the team crossed western lands to the Pacific Ocean, then back again.

LEARN ABOUT SACAGAWEA AS YOU LOOK FOR THESE FUN ITEMS:

- ❏ Armadillo
- ❏ Arrows (2)
- ❏ Bears (2)
- ❏ Beaver
- ❏ Bow
- ❏ Buffalo
- ❏ Deer
- ❏ Drum
- ❏ Eagle
- ❏ Egg
- ❏ Flying bat
- ❏ Flying saucer
- ❏ Frog
- ❏ Groundhog
- ❏ Heart
- ❏ Lost boot
- ❏ Moose
- ❏ Mushroom
- ❏ Owl
- ❏ Rabbits (3)
- ❏ Sailboat
- ❏ Skunk
- ❏ Snake
- ❏ Spear
- ❏ Wild turkey

What does *Sacagawea* mean? Why did she agree to guide Lewis and Clark?

SHE HELPED THE U.S. GAIN THE LAND THAT IS NOW THE STATES OF WASHINGTON, OREGON, IDAHO, MONTANA, AND WYOMING!

KEEP OUR WILDERNESS CLEAN

YOU ARE HERE ✖.

SINCE 2000, U.S. DOLLAR COINS HAVE FEATURED A PICTURE OF SACAGAWEA AND HER INFANT SON.

I'M A ROCKY MOUNTAIN GOAT.

THEY'LL REACH THE PACIFIC OCEAN IN NOVEMBER, 1805.

SACAGAWEA'S NAME MEANS "BIRD WOMAN."

THAT'S A NICE NAME.

I WANT TO SEE THAT!

THEY'LL NAME A RIVER, A MOUNTAIN PEAK, AND A MOUNTAIN PASS AFTER HER!

WELCOME! MY SISTER!

THIS IS THE HOME WHERE I ROAM.

CAMEAHWAIT IS MY BROTHER, CHIEF OF THE SHOSHONE TRIBE.

WE HAVE ORDERS FROM PRESIDENT JEFFERSON TO SURVEY THE NORTHWEST TERRITORY!

ARE THEY STAYING FOR DINNER?

A REAL CHIEF!

HE WILL GIVE US SUPPLIES TO CONTINUE OUR JOURNEY.

I LIKE TO PLAY THE DRUMS.

WEST

WE'LL GIVE THE SHOSHONE GIFTS OF KNIVES, POCKET MIRRORS, SILK RIBBONS, AND SEWING NEEDLES.

I'M A GO FOR

I'M A GOPHER.

WHAT'S THE CONTINENTAL DIVIDE?

IT'S THE RIDGE OF THE ROCKY MOUNTAINS WHICH SEPARATES RIVERS FLOWING IN AN EASTERLY DIRECTION FROM THOSE FLOWING IN A WESTERLY DIRECTION.

SHE WAS BORN IN THE ROCKY MOUNTAINS OF IDAHO!

HOW ABOUT GIVING ME SOME CARROTS?

I'M A GROUND HOG. DO YOU SEE MY SHADOW

HE'S A WISE OLD OWL.

I DIDN'T KNOW THAT!

I'M AN ARMADILLO.

SOME SAY SACAGAWEA LIVED TO BE 100 YEARS OLD.

F

NEIL ARMSTRONG

Neil Alden Armstrong is one of the most famous U.S. astronauts. On July 20, 1969, Armstrong and fellow astronaut Edwin "Buzz" Aldrin Jr. landed the *Eagle*— *Apollo 11*'s lunar module—on the moon's surface. Armstrong became the first person to set foot on the moon.

LEARN ABOUT NEIL ARMSTRONG AS YOU LOOK FOR THESE FUN ITEMS:

- ❑ **Balloon**
- ❑ **Banana peel**
- ❑ **Bird**
- ❑ **Cactus**
- ❑ **Can**
- ❑ **Cloud**
- ❑ **Firecracker**
- ❑ **Fire hydrant**
- ❑ **Fish (3)**
- ❑ **Flashlight**
- ❑ **Flying saucer**
- ❑ **Heart**
- ❑ **Hot-air balloon**
- ❑ **Hot dog**
- ❑ **Ice-cream cone**
- ❑ **Key**
- ❑ **Kite**
- ❑ **Lamp**
- ❑ **Mouse**
- ❑ **Paper airplane**
- ❑ **Pencil**
- ❑ **Police officer**
- ❑ **School bus**
- ❑ **Sock**
- ❑ **Superhero**
- ❑ **Top hat**
- ❑ **Umbrella**
- ❑ **Wagon wheel**

What did Neil Armstrong say when he first set foot on the moon's surface?
About how much would you weigh on the moon?

WASHINGTON, D.C.

George Washington envisioned a city of beauty and stature to serve as the nation's capital. In 1791, he hired Pierre L'Enfant—a French architect and engineer—to design it. L'Enfant's plan served Washington's dream well. The city has wide, straight avenues; lush parks; towering monuments; and beautiful trees and flowers. It also is an important political center, where decisions affecting millions of lives are made daily at the White House (home of the president), the Capitol (home of the U.S. Congress), the Supreme Court, and many federal agencies.

LEARN ABOUT WASHINGTON, D.C., AS YOU LOOK FOR THESE FUN ITEMS:

- ☐ Balloon
- ☐ Baseball cap
- ☐ Bird
- ☐ Cactus
- ☐ Fish
- ☐ Fishbowl
- ☐ Flags (3)
- ☐ Flower
- ☐ Headband
- ☐ Key
- ☐ Kite
- ☐ Mouse
- ☐ Paintbrush
- ☐ Scarves (2)
- ☐ Star
- ☐ Top hat
- ☐ Turtle

What is this city's purpose?

JOAN OF ARC

Joan of Arc was born about 1412. As a child growing up on a farm in France, she was known for her gentleness and holiness. But Jeanne D'Arc, as she is called in France, was destined for greater things.

The English and their allies controlled a large part of France. Guided by her faith, Joan donned the armor of a soldier and bravely led the French army to victories over the English.

LEARN ABOUT JOAN OF ARC AS YOU LOOK FOR THESE FUN ITEMS:

- ☐ Balloon
- ☐ Banana peel
- ☐ Baseball cap
- ☐ Beret
- ☐ Birds (2)
- ☐ Book
- ☐ Bow and arrow
- ☐ Camera
- ☐ Candles (2)
- ☐ Duck
- ☐ Ear of corn
- ☐ Feather
- ☐ Football
- ☐ Football helmet
- ☐ Hammer
- ☐ Hobbyhorse
- ☐ Hockey player
- ☐ Hot dog
- ☐ Ice-cream cone
- ☐ Mouse
- ☐ Paintbrush
- ☐ Propeller
- ☐ Roller skate
- ☐ Slingshot
- ☐ Sock
- ☐ Star
- ☐ Worm

Name the king who made Joan the commander of his troops.
Where was Joan captured?

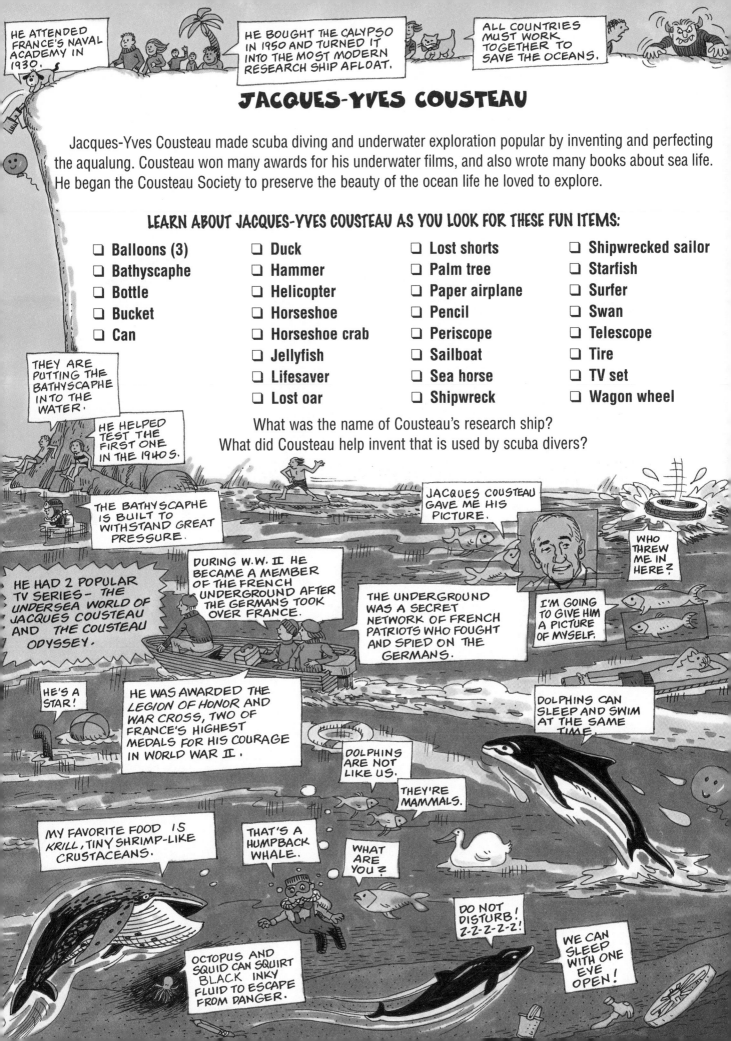

JACQUES-YVES COUSTEAU

Jacques-Yves Cousteau made scuba diving and underwater exploration popular by inventing and perfecting the aqualung. Cousteau won many awards for his underwater films, and also wrote many books about sea life. He began the Cousteau Society to preserve the beauty of the ocean life he loved to explore.

LEARN ABOUT JACQUES-YVES COUSTEAU AS YOU LOOK FOR THESE FUN ITEMS:

- Balloons (3)
- Bathyscaphe
- Bottle
- Bucket
- Can
- Duck
- Hammer
- Helicopter
- Horseshoe
- Horseshoe crab
- Jellyfish
- Lifesaver
- Lost oar
- Lost shorts
- Palm tree
- Paper airplane
- Pencil
- Periscope
- Sailboat
- Sea horse
- Shipwreck
- Shipwrecked sailor
- Starfish
- Surfer
- Swan
- Telescope
- Tire
- TV set
- Wagon wheel

What was the name of Cousteau's research ship?
What did Cousteau help invent that is used by scuba divers?

NEW YORK CITY

New York City is the most populous city in the United States. It is a universal center for art, fashion, architecture, finance, publishing, and more. A great deal of what happens in New York affects what happens around the country and even around the world.

LEARN ABOUT NEW YORK CITY AS YOU LOOK FOR THESE FUN ITEMS:

- ☐ Apple
- ☐ Baseball
- ☐ Bird
- ☐ Blimp
- ☐ Book
- ☐ Boom box
- ☐ Container ship
- ☐ Diver
- ☐ Ferry
- ☐ Fish
- ☐ Flower
- ☐ Flying saucer
- ☐ Football
- ☐ Ghost
- ☐ Heart
- ☐ Helicopter
- ☐ Periscope
- ☐ Rowboat
- ☐ Star
- ☐ Telescope
- ☐ Tire
- ☐ Top hat
- ☐ Tugboat
- ☐ Worm

Who first settled New York?
When was it the nation's capital?

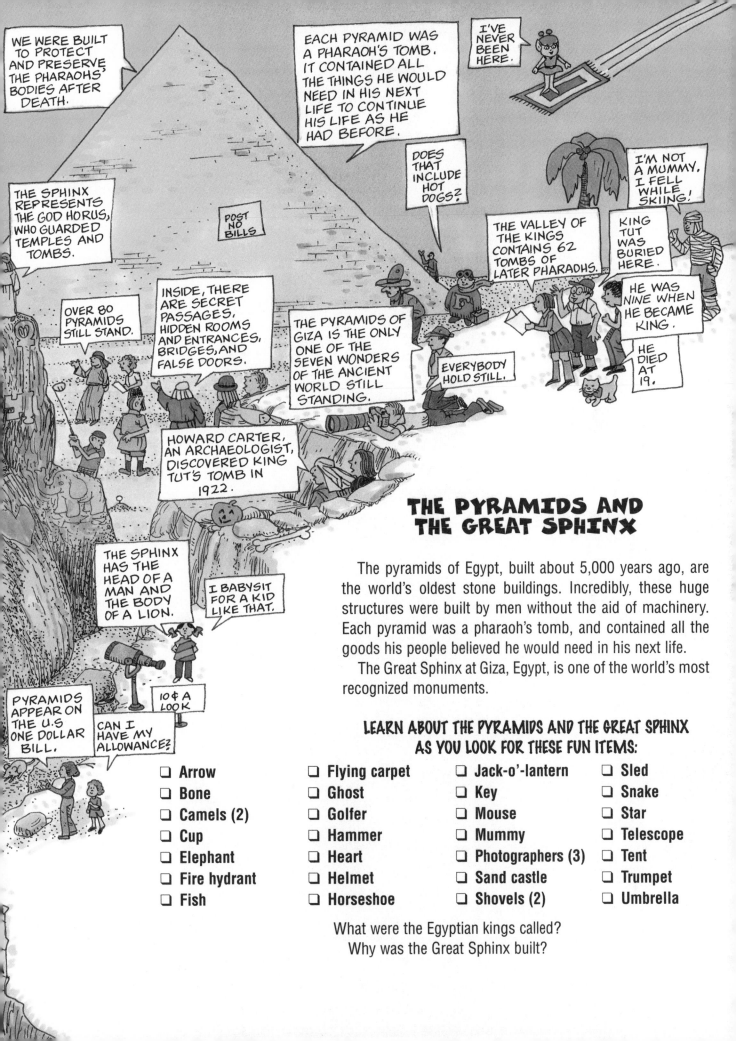

THE PYRAMIDS AND THE GREAT SPHINX

The pyramids of Egypt, built about 5,000 years ago, are the world's oldest stone buildings. Incredibly, these huge structures were built by men without the aid of machinery. Each pyramid was a pharaoh's tomb, and contained all the goods his people believed he would need in his next life.

The Great Sphinx at Giza, Egypt, is one of the world's most recognized monuments.

LEARN ABOUT THE PYRAMIDS AND THE GREAT SPHINX AS YOU LOOK FOR THESE FUN ITEMS:

- ❏ Arrow
- ❏ Bone
- ❏ Camels (2)
- ❏ Cup
- ❏ Elephant
- ❏ Fire hydrant
- ❏ Fish
- ❏ Flying carpet
- ❏ Ghost
- ❏ Golfer
- ❏ Hammer
- ❏ Heart
- ❏ Helmet
- ❏ Horseshoe
- ❏ Jack-o'-lantern
- ❏ Key
- ❏ Mouse
- ❏ Mummy
- ❏ Photographers (3)
- ❏ Sand castle
- ❏ Shovels (2)
- ❏ Sled
- ❏ Snake
- ❏ Star
- ❏ Telescope
- ❏ Tent
- ❏ Trumpet
- ❏ Umbrella

What were the Egyptian kings called?
Why was the Great Sphinx built?

LEONARDO DA VINCI

Leonardo da Vinci (1452–1519) was one of the greatest artists of the Renaissance. However, his interests and accomplishments went far beyond the world of art. He was, at various times, an inventor, scientist, engineer, architect, and designer. Leonardo's investigations marked the beginning of the scientific revolution and paved the way for scientists and inventors who followed him to take their places in history.

SKETCH FOR AN EQUESTRIAN STATUE

LEARN ABOUT LEONARDO DA VINCI AS YOU LOOK FOR THESE FUN ITEMS:

- ❑ Balloon
- ❑ Banana peel
- ❑ Birds (2)
- ❑ Bone
- ❑ Candles (13)
- ❑ Cane
- ❑ Chef
- ❑ Crown
- ❑ Doctor
- ❑ Duck
- ❑ Easel
- ❑ Feather
- ❑ Flowerpot
- ❑ Flying bat

- ❑ Ghost
- ❑ Graduate
- ❑ *La Gioconda*
- ❑ Ladder
- ❑ Lifesaver
- ❑ Lost shoe
- ❑ Mouse
- ❑ Paintbrushes (2)
- ❑ Paint bucket
- ❑ Painted egg
- ❑ Paper airplane
- ❑ Pencil
- ❑ Pizza
- ❑ Screwdriver

- ❑ Skull
- ❑ Snowman
- ❑ Stool
- ❑ Wizard

HUMAN PROPORTIONS RECONSTRUCTED ACCORDING TO VITRUVIUS — 1487-90

For what is the *Mona Lisa* famous?
Why must a mirror be used in order to read Leonardo's notebooks?

ANATOMY-MUSCLES OF UPPER LIMB

PLAN FOR A CHURCH— 1487-89

LEONARDO WAS ALSO AN ARCHITECT, MUSICIAN, MATHEMATICIAN, AND SCULPTOR.

HE'S GOING TO PAINT MY PORTRAIT.

MACHINE FOR MAKING CONCAVE MIRRORS

WELL PUMP

"RENAISSANCE" MEANS "REBIRTH."

IN 1482, HE BECAME COURT ARTIST FOR THE DUKE OF MILAN.

AS A MILITARY ENGINEER FOR THE DUKE, HE DESIGNED A MOVABLE BRIDGE, DIFFERENT TYPES OF LADDERS FOR STORMING AND CLIMBING CASTLE WALLS, ARTILLERY, AND GUNS.

ANATOMY IS THE STUDY OF THE STRUCTURE OF THE BODY.

HIS ARE THE FIRST ACCURATE DRAWINGS OF ANATOMY.

HIS PAINTINGS ARE GRACEFUL, CALM, AND DELICATE.

HE EXPLORED HUMAN ANATOMY AND PERSPECTIVE.

THE FIRST SUCCESSFUL HELICOPTER, DESIGNED IN THE 1930s, WAS BASED ON LEONARDO'S DRAWINGS.

HE BASED HIS DRAWINGS ON THE ACTION OF A SCREW.

HE HAS GREAT POWERS OF OBSERVATION.

I'M LOST!

HE MADE MAPS OF EUROPE.

HE RECORDED HIS IDEAS OF ART, SCIENCE, AND ENGINEERING IN NOTEBOOKS.

HE WROTE HIS NOTES BACKWARD SO THEY CAN ONLY BE READ USING A MIRROR.

YOU ARE HERE X

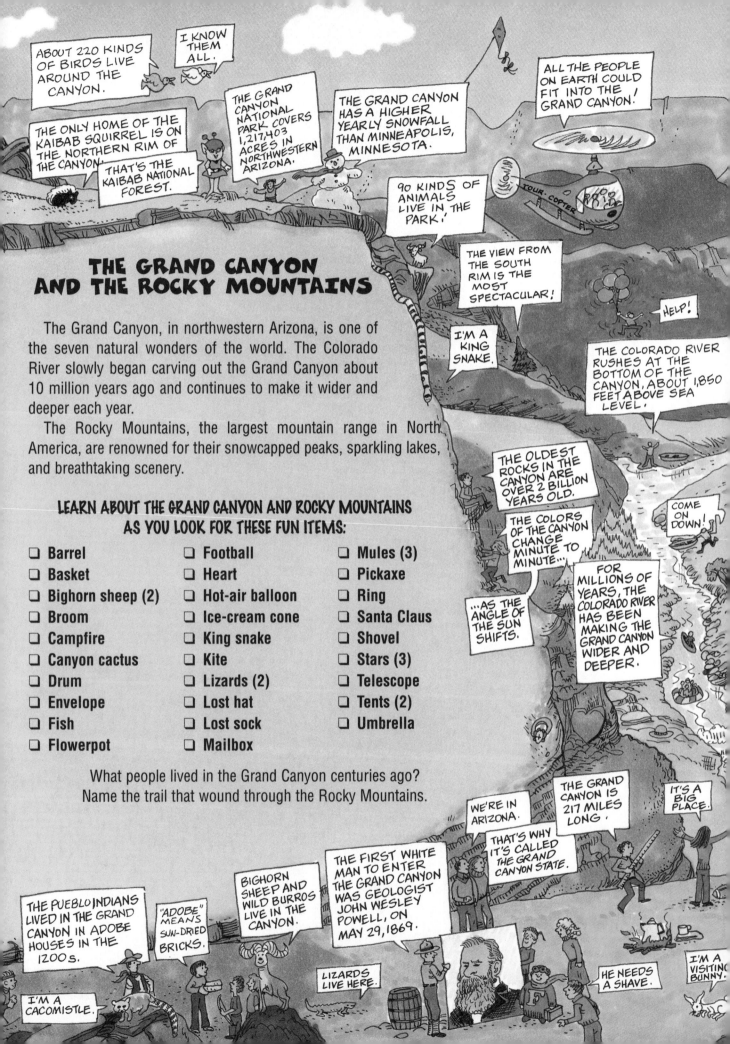

THE GRAND CANYON AND THE ROCKY MOUNTAINS

The Grand Canyon, in northwestern Arizona, is one of the seven natural wonders of the world. The Colorado River slowly began carving out the Grand Canyon about 10 million years ago and continues to make it wider and deeper each year.

The Rocky Mountains, the largest mountain range in North America, are renowned for their snowcapped peaks, sparkling lakes, and breathtaking scenery.

LEARN ABOUT THE GRAND CANYON AND ROCKY MOUNTAINS AS YOU LOOK FOR THESE FUN ITEMS:

- ❑ Barrel
- ❑ Basket
- ❑ Bighorn sheep (2)
- ❑ Broom
- ❑ Campfire
- ❑ Canyon cactus
- ❑ Drum
- ❑ Envelope
- ❑ Fish
- ❑ Flowerpot
- ❑ Football
- ❑ Heart
- ❑ Hot-air balloon
- ❑ Ice-cream cone
- ❑ King snake
- ❑ Kite
- ❑ Lizards (2)
- ❑ Lost hat
- ❑ Lost sock
- ❑ Mailbox
- ❑ Mules (3)
- ❑ Pickaxe
- ❑ Ring
- ❑ Santa Claus
- ❑ Shovel
- ❑ Stars (3)
- ❑ Telescope
- ❑ Tents (2)
- ❑ Umbrella

What people lived in the Grand Canyon centuries ago?
Name the trail that wound through the Rocky Mountains.

THE WORLD'S SEVEN CONTINENTS

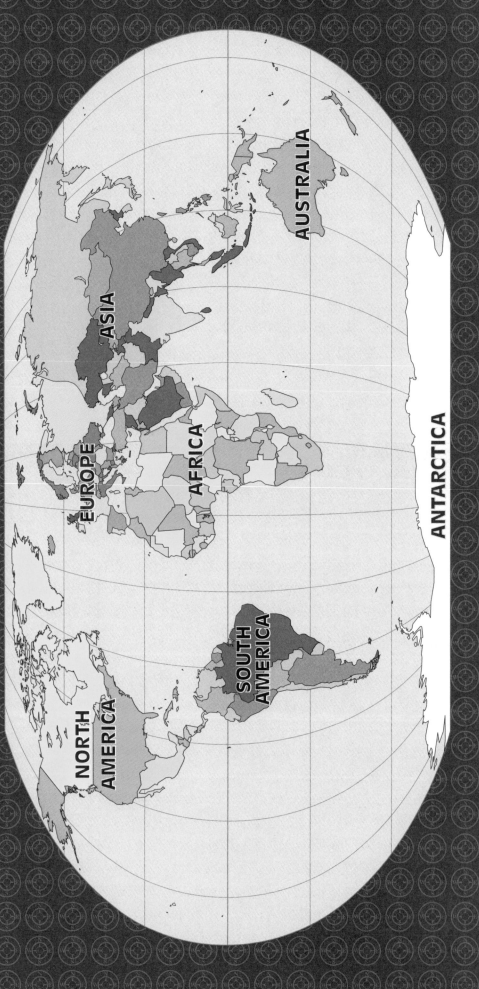

NORTH AMERICA

SOUTH AMERICA

EUROPE

AFRICA

ASIA

AUSTRALIA

ANTARCTICA

Populations are always changing. The populations listed in this book reflect generally accepted population numbers around the world as of 2008.

ASIA, AUSTRALIA, AND OCEANIA

Asia, the largest of the continents, stretches from above the Arctic Circle to below the equator, and from the Ural Mountains in the west to the Pacific Ocean in the east. Asia's lands include some of the coldest, hottest, wettest, and driest places on Earth.

South and east of Asia lie Australia, New Zealand, and many small island nations in the Pacific, most of which lie south of the equator. Together, they form a region that is known as Oceania.

LEARN ABOUT ASIA, AUSTRALIA, AND OCEANIA AS YOU LOOK FOR THESE FUN ITEMS:

- ❑ Bird
- ❑ Coffeepot
- ❑ Elephant
- ❑ Gold
- ❑ Kangaroo
- ❑ Lobster
- ❑ Mermaid
- ❑ Mountain climber
- ❑ Octopus
- ❑ Oil well
- ❑ Penguin
- ❑ Polar bear
- ❑ Sailboat
- ❑ Telescope

THE 62 TALLEST MOUNTAINS IN THE WORLD ARE IN ASIA.

THE HIGHEST (MT. EVEREST) AND THE LOWEST (DEAD SEA) POINTS ON EARTH ARE LOCATED IN ASIA.

THE WORLD'S MAJOR RELIGIONS BEGAN IN ASIA.

THE GOBI DESERT COVERS ABOUT 500,000 SQUARE MILES.

THE EARLIEST RECORDED CIVILIZATION AROSE IN THE AREA FROM THE MEDITERRANEAN SEA THROUGH SYRIA AND IRAQ TO THE PERSIAN GULF.

IT'S THAT WAY!

KARA SEA

VENISEY RIVER

URAL MOUNTAINS

OB RIVER

AZERBAIJAN

UZBEKISTAN

KAZAKHSTAN

TAJIKISTAN

GEORGIA

ARMENIA

BLACK SEA

CASPIAN SEA

TURKMENISTAN

TURKEY

SYRIA

AFGHANISTAN

LEBANON

ISRAEL

IRAQ

IRAN

KUWAIT

PAKISTAN

JORDAN

DEAD SEA

PERSIAN GULF

SAUDI ARABIA

RED SEA

UNITED ARAB EMIRATES

OMAN

YEMEN

ARABIAN SEA

QATAR

EUROPE

MEDITERRANEAN SEA

AFRICA

ATLANTIC OCEAN

NORTH

SOUTH

WEST

EAST

RUSSIA TAKES UP ONE SEVENTH OF THE WORLD'S TOTAL LAND AREA AND HAS THE EIGHTH LARGEST POPULATION.

TWO-THIRDS OF RUSSIA'S POPULATION LIVES IN EUROPE, WHILE ONLY A THIRD LIVES IN ASIA.

SNOW COVERS MORE THAN HALF OF RUSSIA FOR SIX MONTHS OF THE YEAR.

BARENTS SEA

KARA SEA

RUSSIA

FORESTS COVER MORE THAN HALF THE COUNTRY.

WHITE SEA

CARS AND TRACTORS MANUFACTURING

URAL MTS

THE URAL MTS. DIVIDE RUSSIA BETWEEN EUROPE AND ASIA.

YENISEY RIVER

LAKE ONEGA

BALTIC SEA

LAKE LADOGA

ST. BASIL'S CATHEDRAL

GULF OF FINLAND

POTATOES

WHEAT

MOSCOW

OUR POPULATION IS 15,200,000.

OUR LANGUAGES ARE KAZAKH AND RUSSIAN.

WE ARE ALMOST TWICE THE SIZE OF ALASKA.

THE REGION THAT LIES BETWEEN THE BLACK SEA AND THE CASPIAN SEA IS CALLED THE CAUCASUS.

OUR COUNTRY IS MAINLY STEPPE (A VAST SEMI-ARID PLAIN), DESERT, AND MOUNTAIN.

BOLSHOI BALLET

GEORGIA'S POPULATION IS 4,650,000.

ITS WARM CLIMATE ATTRACTS TOURISTS.

KAZAKHSTAN

ALTAY MTS

THE MAIN SPACE CENTER FOR THE COMMONWEALTH IS LOCATED HERE.

ITS LANGUAGES ARE GEORGIAN, RUSSIAN, ARMENIAN, AND AZERI.

TBILISI

OIL

CASPIAN SEA

UZBEKISTAN

ASTANA

95% OF OUR COUNTRY IS MOUNTAINOUS.

TASHKENT

BISHKEK

KYRGYZSTAN

BLACK SEA

GEORGIA

BAKU

ASHGABAT

90% IS COVERED BY KARA-KUM DESERT.

COMMUNISM PEAK (24,590 FT)

ARMENIA

TAJIKISTAN

OUR POPULATION IS 7,300,000, AND OUR LANGUAGE IS TAJIK (ALSO RUSSIAN).

MEDITERRANEAN SEA

YEREVAN

AZERBAIJAN

TURKMENISTAN

DUSHANBE

THE LANGUAGES OF AZERBAIJAN ARE AZERI, RUSSIAN, AND ARMENIAN.

THEIR POPULATION IS 8,200,000.

ARMENIA IS THE MOST INDUSTRIALIZED STATE IN THE CAUCASUS.

TURKMENISTAN'S POPULATION IS 5,200,000, AND ITS LANGUAGES ARE TURKMEN, RUSSIAN, AND UZBEK.

RUSSIA AND ITS NEIGHBORS

ITS POPULATION IS 3,000,000.

MAIN LANGUAGES SPOKEN ARE ARMENIAN AND RUSSIAN.

Russia, the world's largest country, spans two continents. It covers more than 50 percent of Europe and more than 35 percent of Asia.

Russia used to be part of an even bigger nation called the Soviet Union, which broke apart in 1991. Many of the countries to Russia's south, now independent, also were part of the Soviet Union until 1991.

EUROPE

ASIA

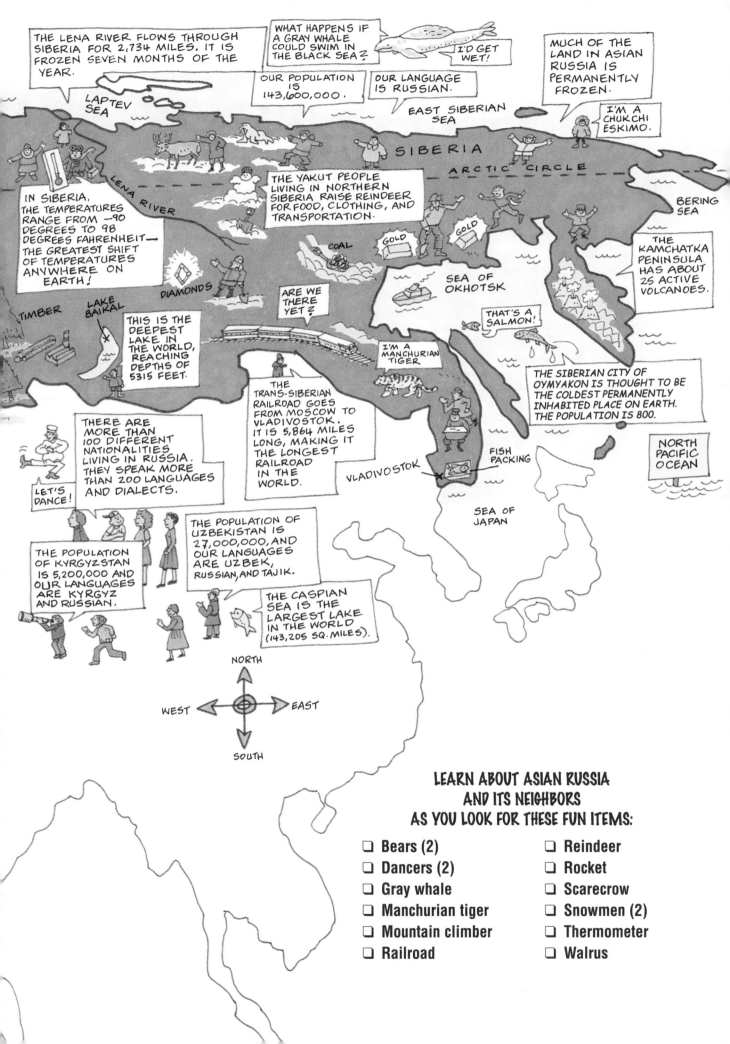

LEARN ABOUT ASIAN RUSSIA
AND ITS NEIGHBORS
AS YOU LOOK FOR THESE FUN ITEMS:

- ❑ Bears (2)
- ❑ Dancers (2)
- ❑ Gray whale
- ❑ Manchurian tiger
- ❑ Mountain climber
- ❑ Railroad
- ❑ Reindeer
- ❑ Rocket
- ❑ Scarecrow
- ❑ Snowmen (2)
- ❑ Thermometer
- ❑ Walrus

TURKEY AND CYPRUS

Three percent of Turkey's land area lies in Europe. The rest is in Asia, in a region known as Anatolia or Asia Minor. Istanbul, which is Turkey's largest city, is the only city in the world that occupies land on two continents.

Cyprus is only 140 miles long at its longest point, and 60 miles wide at its widest point. It has long been controlled by other nations, and Greece and Turkey both still claim parts of it.

LEARN ABOUT TURKEY AND CYPRUS AS YOU LOOK FOR THESE FUN ITEMS:

- ☐ Apples
- ☐ Ball
- ☐ Bears (3)
- ☐ Book
- ☐ Cook
- ☐ Cowboy
- ☐ Egg
- ☐ Fish
- ☐ Goats (5)
- ☐ Grapes
- ☐ Ibis
- ☐ Ladder
- ☐ Sailboats (3)
- ☐ Shepherd
- ☐ Tea bag
- ☐ Telescope
- ☐ Tin Man
- ☐ Umbrellas (2)

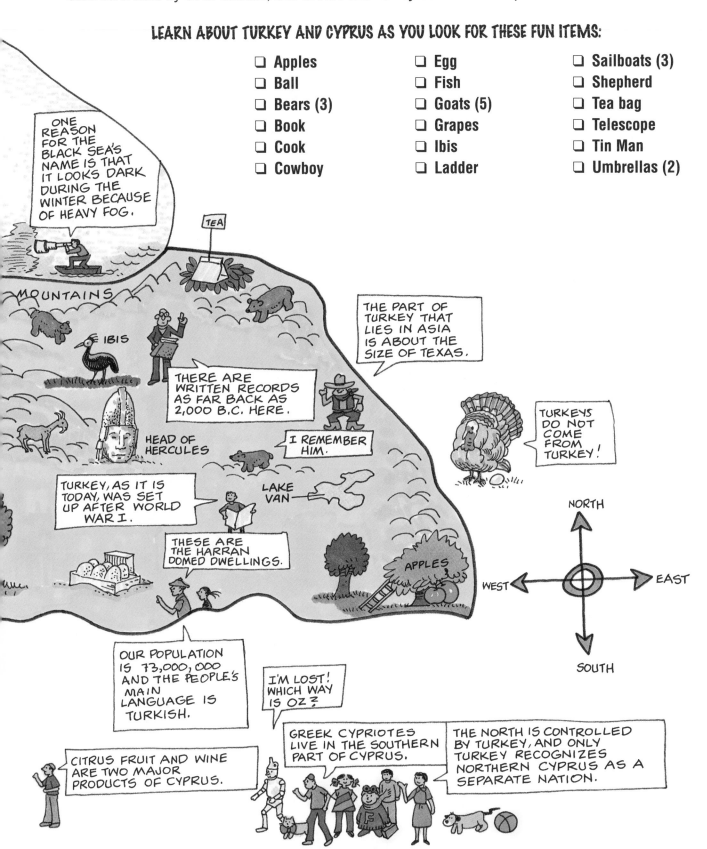

THE MIDDLE EAST

This part of Asia, in the area between the Tigris and Euphrates rivers, was one of the first places where civilization was recorded. Towns and communities were thriving here 6,000 years ago. The Arabian Peninsula *(see pp. 12-13)* is also part of the Middle East—a region that has about 75 percent of the world's oil reserves.

THE ARABIAN PENINSULA

The Arabian Peninsula is home to six independent countries. (Saudi Arabia is the largest and Bahrain the smallest.) The lion's share of the world's oil is in this region. Saudi Arabia alone has 26 percent of the world's known oil reserves.

The peninsula also is where you will find the world's largest continuous sand desert, an area known as "the Empty Quarter." Sand dunes there reach as high as 600 feet.

LEARN ABOUT THE ARABIAN PENINSULA AS YOU LOOK FOR THESE FUN ITEMS:

- ❏ Basketball
- ❏ Coffeepot
- ❏ Coral
- ❏ Horses (2)
- ❏ Moon
- ❏ Oar
- ❏ Rose
- ❏ Sardines
- ❏ Scarecrow
- ❏ Shark fins (2)
- ❏ Soccer ball
- ❏ Tent
- ❏ Thermometers (2)
- ❏ Umbrella

THE INDIAN SUBCONTINENT

South-central Asia—where a large area of land juts into the Indian Ocean—is referred to as the Indian subcontinent. About 70 percent of the people in this heavily populated region depend on the land for their livelihood.

India is one of only two countries in the world with more than one billion people. (China is the other.) The other countries in this region are Afghanistan, Pakistan, Nepal, Bhutan, Bangladesh, and Sri Lanka. About 400 miles southwest of Sri Lanka is a group of small islands that make up the country of Maldives.

LEARN ABOUT THE INDIAN SUBCONTINENT AS YOU LOOK FOR THESE FUN ITEMS:

- ❑ Bear
- ❑ Camels (2)
- ❑ Carpets (2)
- ❑ Cow
- ❑ Dancer
- ❑ Elephants (2)
- ❑ Fish (2)
- ❑ Monkeys (2)
- ❑ Musicians (2)
- ❑ Peanuts
- ❑ Pepper
- ❑ Snakes (2)
- ❑ Soccer ball
- ❑ Rhinoceros
- ❑ Turtle
- ❑ Umbrella

MT. EVEREST SITS ON THE BORDER BETWEEN NEPAL AND TIBET.

THE POPULATION OF BHUTAN IS 2,300,000.

THEY SPEAK DZONGKHA.

ONLY 3% OF THIS RUGGED, MOUNTAINOUS LAND IS ARABLE.

NEPAL HAS 8 OF THE WORLD'S 10 HIGHEST MOUNTAINS.

BHUTAN

KATHMANDU

THIMPHU

INDIAN RHINO

GANGES RIVER

RICE

TEA

ONLY 10% OF THE PEOPLE LIVE IN CITIES.

WE ARE ABOUT 1/3 THE SIZE OF THE U.S.

RICE

DHAKA

BANGLADESH

THE POPULATION OF BANGLADESH IS 147,000,000 AND OUR LANGUAGES ARE BANGLA AND ENGLISH.

UNTIL 1971, BANGLADESH WAS PART OF PAKISTAN.

COAL

IT'S GOING TO RAIN.

BANGLADESH'S BIGGEST EXPORT IS JUTE.

BAY OF BENGAL

THE PEOPLE OF NEPAL SPEAK NEPALI, LOCAL DIALECTS, AND ENGLISH.

SOME PLACES IN INDIA AVERAGE MORE THAN 450 INCHES OF RAIN A YEAR!

THIS IS THE ONLY WAY TO TRAVEL.

COLOMBO

SRI LANKA

OUR POPULATION IS 20,250,000.

WE SPEAK SINHALA, TAMIL, AND ENGLISH.

NORTH

WEST   EAST

SOUTH

THE ANIMALS FOUND HERE INCLUDE:

ELEPHANTS, MONKEYS, BEARS, CROCODILES

CHINA AND NORTHEASTERN ASIA

China is the world's third-largest country in land area and first in population. (One out of every five people on Earth lives in China.) Much of China and the Korean peninsula is mountainous. The world's highest mountains, the Himalayas, are in Tibet, a region of China.

LEARN ABOUT CHINA AND NORTHEASTERN ASIA AS YOU LOOK FOR THESE FUN ITEMS:

- ❑ Bicycles (5)
- ❑ Camel
- ❑ Clay soldiers
- ❑ Ducks (3)
- ❑ Flying saucer
- ❑ Genghis Khan
- ❑ Horse
- ❑ Junk
- ❑ Mongol tent
- ❑ Pandas (2)
- ❑ Vulture
- ❑ Yaks (2)

JAPAN

Japan consists of four main islands and about 4,000 smaller ones. This leading industrial country, which is almost as large as California, is densely populated. Most of the people live in the big cities on Honshu Island and in the flat coastal areas.

LEARN ABOUT JAPAN AS YOU LOOK FOR THESE FUN ITEMS:

- ☐ Anchovies
- ☐ Baseball bat
- ☐ Brown bear
- ☐ Cod
- ☐ Cook
- ☐ Crab
- ☐ Cranes (2)
- ☐ Dollar sign
- ☐ Golfer
- ☐ Octopus
- ☐ Skier
- ☐ Snake
- ☐ Snow sculpture
- ☐ Squid
- ☐ Sumo wrestler
- ☐ Tofu
- ☐ Turtle
- ☐ Umbrellas (2)

SOUTHEAST ASIA

This region is close to the equator, giving it a tropical climate with periods of heavy rainfall. Dense jungles or tropical rain forests cover much of the area, which has three main types of landscape: mountains, plains, or high, flat areas called plateaus. Most people here live near water—oceans, seas, or mighty rivers. Many Southeast Asians use the waterways for irrigating farmland, fishing, and transportation.

LEARN ABOUT SOUTHEAST ASIA AS YOU LOOK FOR THESE FUN ITEMS:

- ❑ Brown bears (2)
- ❑ Cyclists (3)
- ❑ Dancers
- ❑ Deer
- ❑ Elephant
- ❑ Fisherman
- ❑ Flying fish
- ❑ "Giraffe" necked woman
- ❑ Lobster
- ❑ Pitchfork
- ❑ Scarecrow
- ❑ Tiger
- ❑ Umbrellas (2)

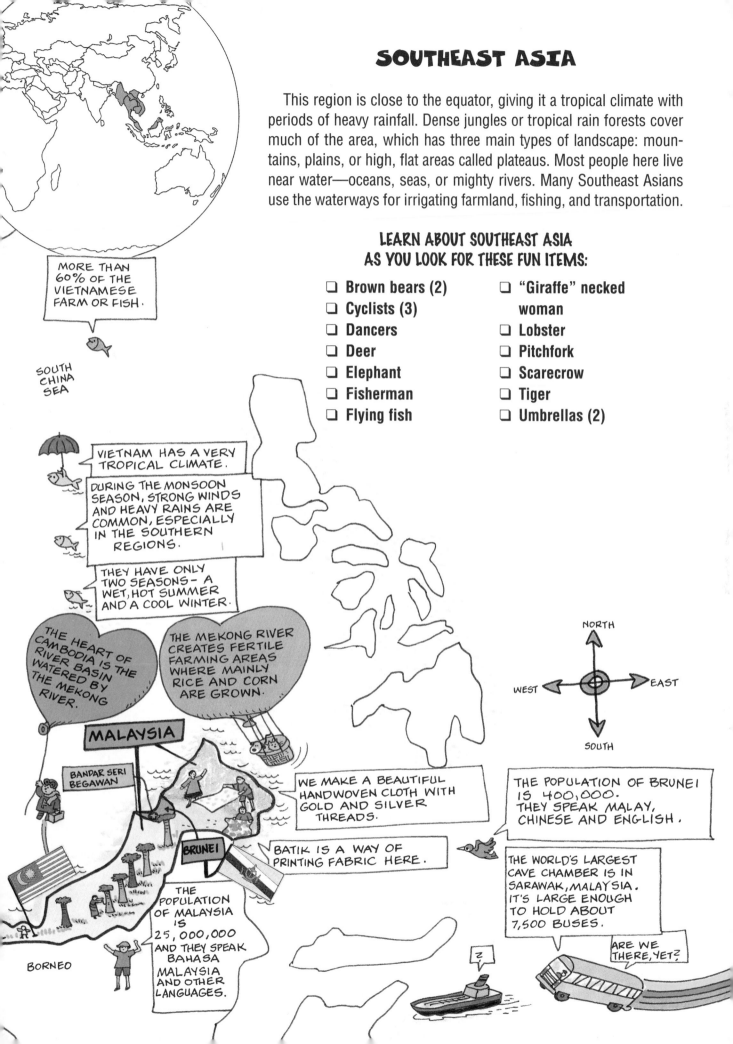

MORE THAN 60% OF THE VIETNAMESE FARM OR FISH.

SOUTH CHINA SEA

VIETNAM HAS A VERY TROPICAL CLIMATE.

DURING THE MONSOON SEASON, STRONG WINDS AND HEAVY RAINS ARE COMMON, ESPECIALLY IN THE SOUTHERN REGIONS.

THEY HAVE ONLY TWO SEASONS – A WET, HOT SUMMER AND A COOL WINTER.

THE HEART OF CAMBODIA IS THE RIVER BASIN WATERED BY THE MEKONG RIVER.

THE MEKONG RIVER CREATES FERTILE FARMING AREAS WHERE MAINLY RICE AND CORN ARE GROWN.

NORTH
WEST EAST
SOUTH

MALAYSIA

BANDAR SERI BEGAWAN

WE MAKE A BEAUTIFUL HANDWOVEN CLOTH WITH GOLD AND SILVER THREADS.

THE POPULATION OF BRUNEI IS 400,000. THEY SPEAK MALAY, CHINESE AND ENGLISH.

BRUNEI

BATIK IS A WAY OF PRINTING FABRIC HERE.

THE WORLD'S LARGEST CAVE CHAMBER IS IN SARAWAK, MALAYSIA. IT'S LARGE ENOUGH TO HOLD ABOUT 7,500 BUSES.

THE POPULATION OF MALAYSIA IS 25,000,000 AND THEY SPEAK BAHASA MALAYSIA AND OTHER LANGUAGES.

BORNEO

ARE WE THERE, YET?

INDONESIA and PACIFIC ISLAND NATIONS

Indonesia, Singapore, the Philippines, and East Timor are part of Asia. Papua New Guinea and many small island nations scattered in this area of the Pacific Ocean are part of a region called Oceania. *(See p. 5 for a list of all the countries of Oceania.)* Most of this area has a hot, wet, tropical climate.

LEARN ABOUT INDONESIA AND PACIFIC ISLAND NATIONS AS YOU LOOK FOR THESE FUN ITEMS:

- ☐ Airplane
- ☐ Coffeepot
- ☐ Kite
- ☐ Orangutan
- ☐ Photographer
- ☐ Rhinoceros
- ☐ Shark fins (4)
- ☐ Tiger
- ☐ Tree kangaroo
- ☐ Turtle
- ☐ Tuna
- ☐ Volcanoes (2)

THE CLIMATE IS HOT AND HUMID.

OVER 80° IS THE AVERAGE TEMPERATURE.

THERE ARE OVER 7,000 ISLANDS IN THE PHILIPPINES. MOST OF THE PEOPLE LIVE ON THESE 11 ISLANDS.

BONIN ISLANDS (JAPAN)

OF ABOUT 25,000 ISLANDS IN THE PACIFIC OCEAN, ONLY A FEW THOUSAND ARE INHABITED.

NORTHERN MARIANA ISLANDS (U.S.)

WAKE ISLAND (U.S.)

NORTH PACIFIC OCEAN

PALAU

SOME OF THE PACIFIC ISLANDS MAKE UP NINE INDEPENDENT COUNTRIES.

MANY OTHER ISLANDS ARE GOVERNED BY COUNTRIES SUCH AS THE U.S., GREAT BRITAIN, AND FRANCE.

MARSHALL ISLANDS

VOLCANIC ERUPTIONS ARE COMMON. THESE ISLANDS ARE ACTUALLY THE TOPS OF MOUNTAINS THAT ARE STILL FORMING.

MICRONESIA

SOME OF THE ISLANDS ARE THE TIPS OF MOUNTAINS OR VOLCANOES, OTHERS ARE MADE UP OF CORAL.

I'M A PEARL OYSTER.

KIRIBATI

EQUATOR

PAPUA NEW GUINEA

OUR POPULATION IS 5,600,000, AND OUR LANGUAGES ARE ENGLISH, PIDGIN ENGLISH, MOTU, AND MANY OTHERS.

MOLUCCA SEA

INDONESIA

RAINFALL IS OVER 100 INCHES ANNUALLY.

HALF THE ISLAND BELONGS TO INDONESIA.

BISMARCK SEA

MT. WILHELM (14,790 FT)

TREE KANGAROO

BANDA SEA

INDONESIA'S MAIN EXPORTS ARE OIL, TIMBER, RUBBER AND COFFEE.

TUVALU

SOLOMON ISLANDS

DILI

EAST TIMOR

EAST TIMOR'S LANGUAGES ARE TETUM, PORTUGUESE, INDONESIAN, ENGLISH, AND OTHERS.

EAST TIMOR— THE WORLD'S NEWEST COUNTRY —BECAME INDEPENDENT IN 2002.

VANUATU

PORT MORESBY

FIJI

EAST TIMOR'S POPULATION IS 1,050,000.

ARAFURA SEA

CORAL SEA IS. (AUS.)

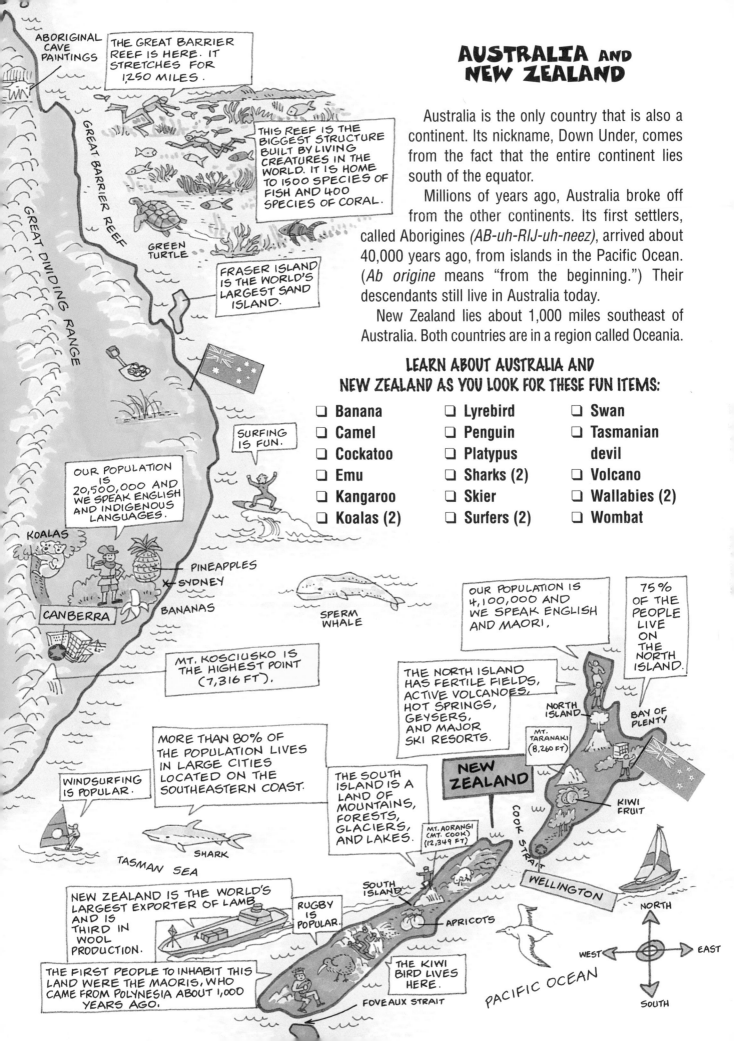

AUSTRALIA AND NEW ZEALAND

Australia is the only country that is also a continent. Its nickname, Down Under, comes from the fact that the entire continent lies south of the equator.

Millions of years ago, Australia broke off from the other continents. Its first settlers, called Aborigines *(AB-uh-RIJ-uh-neez)*, arrived about 40,000 years ago, from islands in the Pacific Ocean. (*Ab origine* means "from the beginning.") Their descendants still live in Australia today.

New Zealand lies about 1,000 miles southeast of Australia. Both countries are in a region called Oceania.

LEARN ABOUT AUSTRALIA AND NEW ZEALAND AS YOU LOOK FOR THESE FUN ITEMS:

- ☐ Banana
- ☐ Camel
- ☐ Cockatoo
- ☐ Emu
- ☐ Kangaroo
- ☐ Koalas (2)
- ☐ Lyrebird
- ☐ Penguin
- ☐ Platypus
- ☐ Sharks (2)
- ☐ Skier
- ☐ Surfers (2)
- ☐ Swan
- ☐ Tasmanian devil
- ☐ Volcano
- ☐ Wallabies (2)
- ☐ Wombat

AFRICA

Once an unexplored and mysterious place to Europeans, Africa was known as the "Dark Continent." By the 19th century, European powers influenced or controlled much of Africa. However, starting in the late 1950s, country after country in Africa achieved its independence. The continent now is home to 53 independent nations. Africa's newest country, Eritrea, became independent in 1993, when it split from Ethiopia.

LEARN ABOUT AFRICA AS YOU LOOK FOR THESE FUN ITEMS:

- ❏ Atlas Mountains
- ❏ Butterfly
- ❏ Cape of Good Hope
- ❏ Elephant
- ❏ Gold bar
- ❏ Indian Ocean

- ❏ Mount Kilimanjaro
- ❏ Nile River
- ❏ Oil wells (2)
- ❏ Palm trees (4)
- ❏ Pyramid
- ❏ Rain cloud

- ❏ Rhinoceros
- ❏ Sea horse
- ❏ Sheep (2)
- ❏ Suez Canal
- ❏ Umbrella
- ❏ Zebra

NORTHERN AFRICA

The peoples of ancient Greece, Rome, and Arabia influenced cultures in this part of Africa, and African culture—especially that of ancient Egypt—influenced them. In northern Africa today, Arabic is the dominant language and Islam is the major religion. Although Egypt is on the African continent, politically it often is considered part of the region known as the Middle East.

LEARN ABOUT NORTHERN AFRICA AS YOU LOOK FOR THESE FUN ITEMS:

- ❑ Barbary ape
- ❑ Beret
- ❑ Boats (3)
- ❑ Bunch of grapes
- ❑ Hyena
- ❑ Miner
- ❑ Mummy
- ❑ Orange tree
- ❑ Oil wells (4)
- ❑ Ostrich
- ❑ Palm trees (3)
- ❑ Pencil
- ❑ Pirate
- ❑ Pyramids (4)
- ❑ Scarecrow
- ❑ Scorpion
- ❑ Shovel
- ❑ Snake
- ❑ Thermometer

THE SAHEL

Just south of the Sahara Desert is a region called the Sahel, long inhabited by animal grazers and farmers. Much of the area is changing into desert as the Sahara expands southward at a rate of about three miles a year.

LEARN ABOUT THE SAHEL AS YOU LOOK FOR THESE FUN ITEMS:

- ☐ Anchor
- ☐ Basket
- ☐ Bird
- ☐ Camels (5)
- ☐ Cotton balls (3)
- ☐ Goat
- ☐ Elephant
- ☐ Fisherman
- ☐ Hippopotamus
- ☐ Lake Chad
- ☐ Niger River
- ☐ Peanuts (3)
- ☐ Periscope
- ☐ Soccer ball
- ☐ Sun
- ☐ Tent

THE HORN OF AFRICA

The region along Africa's northeastern coast is known as the Horn of Africa. On maps, its shape looks like the horn of a rhinoceros jutting into the Indian Ocean.

LEARN ABOUT THE HORN OF AFRICA AS YOU LOOK FOR THESE FUN ITEMS:

- ❑ Aardvark
- ❑ Acacia tree
- ❑ Banana
- ❑ Coffeepot
- ❑ Cotton
- ❑ Giraffes (2)
- ❑ Horseshoe
- ❑ Lion
- ❑ Marshmallow
- ❑ Nile crocodile
- ❑ Nubian Desert
- ❑ Oryx
- ❑ Ostrich
- ❑ Red Sea
- ❑ Umbrella
- ❑ White Nile
- ❑ Zebra

THE UPPER WEST COAST

Africa's upper west coast—the part that, seen on a map, bulges out into the Atlantic Ocean—has a landscape that varies from humid coastal plains and swamps to forested hills and plateaus. The soil is fertile, and farmers in this area grow such crops as cocoa, coffee, and peanuts.

During the era of the slave trade to the Americas, and for centuries before with other nations, coastal kingdoms of West Africa grew rich by trading slaves, gold, and ivory with Europeans.

LEARN ABOUT AFRICA'S UPPER WEST COAST AS YOU LOOK FOR THESE FUN ITEMS:

- ❑ Boats (4)
- ❑ Chocolate bar
- ❑ Coffeepot
- ❑ Crocodile
- ❑ Diamonds (4)
- ❑ Elephants
- ❑ Fisherman
- ❑ Game warden
- ❑ Gold bars (3)
- ❑ Lake Volta
- ❑ Lion
- ❑ Miner
- ❑ Pygmy hippopotamus
- ❑ Rain clouds (2)
- ❑ Umbrella

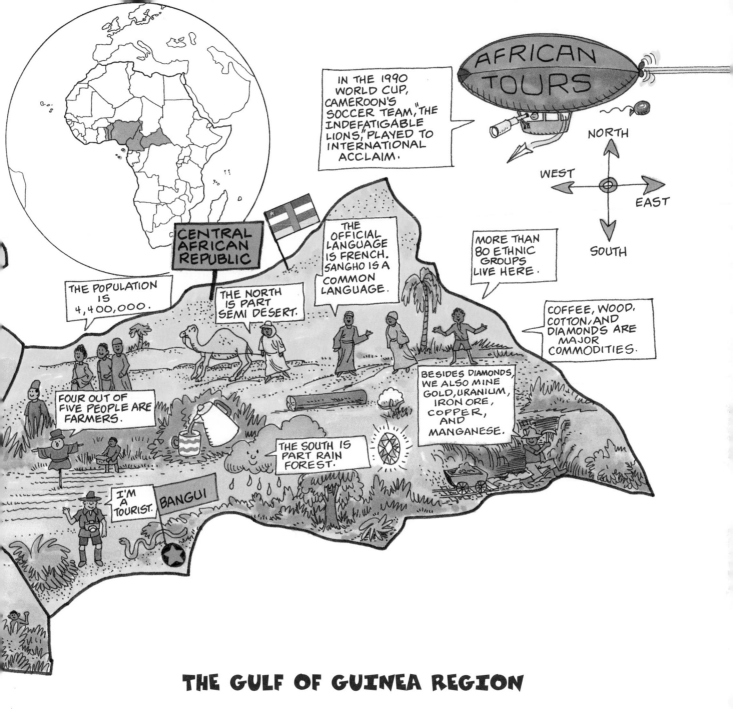

THE GULF OF GUINEA REGION

The Gulf of Guinea is a large section of the Atlantic that lies in the curve of Africa's bulging upper west coast. Many of the countries in this region share the "slave coast" history of the upper west coast countries (pp. 34-35). The gulf region has a richly varied landscape that includes old volcanic mountains, semidesert areas, swamps, tropical rain forests, and savannas. (*Savanna* is tropical or subtropical grassland.)

LEARN ABOUT AFRICA'S GULF OF GUINEA REGION AS YOU LOOK FOR THESE FUN ITEMS:

- ❑ Camera
- ❑ Cup
- ❑ Fishing poles (2)
- ❑ Giraffe
- ❑ Huts (2)
- ❑ Life preserver
- ❑ Oil wells (3)
- ❑ Paper airplane
- ❑ Red car
- ❑ Scarecrow
- ❑ Shark
- ❑ Snakes (2)
- ❑ Telescope
- ❑ Umbrellas (2)
- ❑ Volcano

EQUATORIAL AFRICA

These countries all lie on or very near the equator. A ridge of high land runs down along Lake Albert and Lake Tanganyika, splitting the region. West of the ridge are Equatorial Guinea, Gabon, Congo Republic, and the Democratic Republic of Congo. Much of the land in these countries is tropical rain forest. On and east of the ridge are Uganda, Rwanda, Burundi, Kenya, and Tanzania. The land there ranges from rain forest in the highlands to broad savanna (grasslands), where occasional dry spells can make water scarce for wildlife and humans alike.

**LEARN ABOUT EQUATORIAL AFRICA
AS YOU LOOK FOR THESE FUN ITEMS:**

- ❑ Coffeepot
- ❑ Congo River
- ❑ Crocodile
- ❑ Elephants (4)
- ❑ Gorilla
- ❑ Lake Tanganyika
- ❑ Lion
- ❑ Mount Kilimanjaro
- ❑ Parrot
- ❑ Peacock
- ❑ Snake
- ❑ Umbrellas (3)
- ❑ Zanzibar
- ❑ Zebra

ANGOLA, ZAMBIA, MALAWI, AND MOZAMBIQUE

The region that lies south of the equatorial rain forests, between the South Atlantic Ocean and the Indian Ocean, has lots of open savanna and many farms. The area is home to antelope, elephants, giraffes, zebras, and many other animals.

LEARN ABOUT ANGOLA, ZAMBIA, MALAWI, AND MOZAMBIQUE AS YOU LOOK FOR THESE FUN ITEMS:

- ❏ Bananas (2)
- ❏ Cars (2)
- ❏ Coffee cups (2)
- ❏ Cow
- ❏ Eyeglasses
- ❏ Fish (3)
- ❏ Giraffe
- ❏ Hornbill
- ❏ Kariba Dam
- ❏ Leopard
- ❏ Rhinoceros
- ❏ Rice farmer
- ❏ Ring
- ❏ Scarecrow
- ❏ Shovel
- ❏ Snakes (2)
- ❏ Sun
- ❏ Victoria Falls

NAMIBIA, BOTSWANA, AND ZIMBABWE

Rich deposits of diamonds, gold, and minerals make this area one of the fastest-growing economic regions in Africa. Though rich in natural resources, such as diamonds and minerals, very little of the land in Namibia and Botswana is habitable. Namibia has only six people per square mile and Botswana has only seven. With its more-arable land and better-developed industries, Zimbabwe has 82 people per square mile.

LEARN ABOUT NAMIBIA, BOTSWANA, AND ZIMBABWE AS YOU LOOK FOR THESE FUN ITEMS:

- ☐ Baby
- ☐ Billboard
- ☐ Book
- ☐ Elephants (6)
- ☐ Fishing pole
- ☐ Lions (2)
- ☐ Lost snowman
- ☐ Namib Desert
- ☐ Oryx
- ☐ Picks (2)
- ☐ Rake
- ☐ Scorpion
- ☐ Shipwreck
- ☐ Snakes (5)
- ☐ Sneaker
- ☐ Snowman
- ☐ Truck
- ☐ Zebras (2)

SOUTH AFRICA, LESOTHO, AND SWAZILAND

The world's greatest diamond and gold mines are in South Africa, making it the richest country in Africa. The mines employ tens of thousands of men from neighboring countries.

Lesotho and Swaziland are two small, landlocked countries. One is completely surrounded by South Africa; the other is mostly so. Both are completely dependent on South Africa and Mozambique for trade routes to the ocean and other countries.

LEARN ABOUT SOUTH AFRICA, LESOTHO, AND SWAZILAND AS YOU LOOK FOR THESE FUN ITEMS:

- ❑ Cars (4)
- ❑ Citrus fruit
- ❑ Crown
- ❑ Drummer
- ❑ Giraffes (3)
- ❑ Grapes
- ❑ Guitar
- ❑ Lion
- ❑ Orange River
- ❑ Ostrich
- ❑ Pineapple
- ❑ Sailor
- ❑ Scarecrow
- ❑ Sheep (2)
- ❑ Shovel
- ❑ Table Mountain
- ❑ Tent
- ❑ Tractor
- ❑ Zebra
- ❑ Zulu warrior

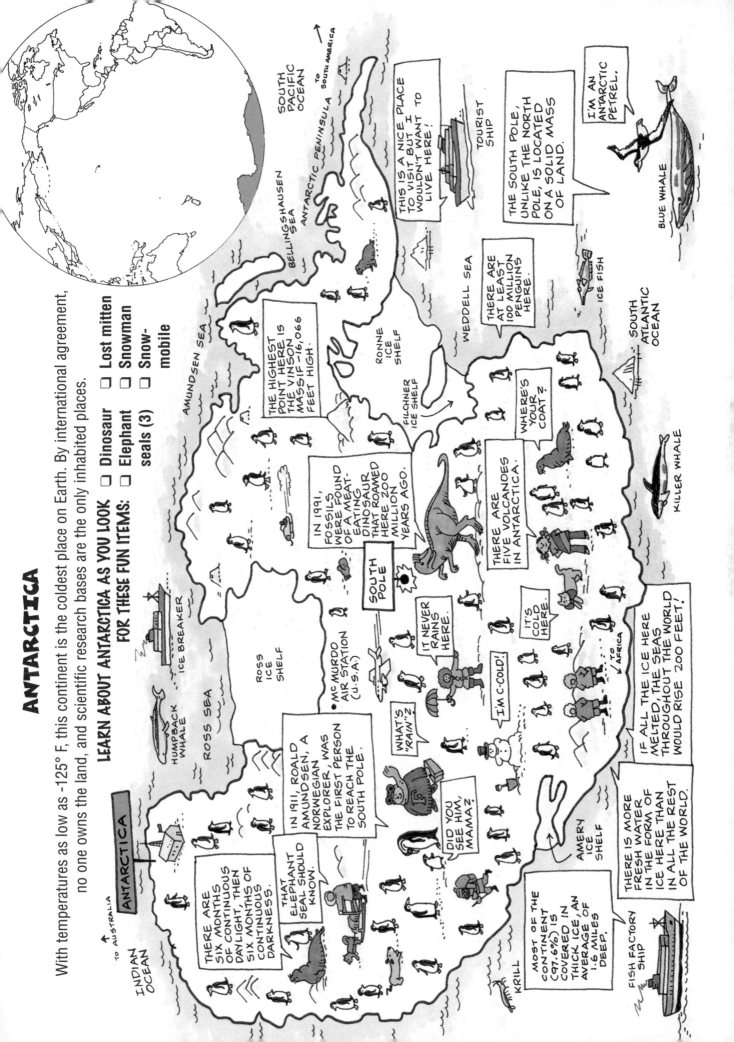

ANTARCTICA

With temperatures as low as -125° F, this continent is the coldest place on Earth. By international agreement, no one owns the land, and scientific research bases are the only inhabited places.

LEARN ABOUT ANTARCTICA AS YOU LOOK FOR THESE FUN ITEMS:

- ☐ Dinosaur
- ☐ Elephant seals (3)
- ☐ Lost mitten
- ☐ Snowman
- ☐ Snow-mobile

NORTH AMERICA AND SOUTH AMERICA

North America is the third largest of the seven continents. It stretches from Greenland and Canada in the Arctic north to Panama, which is near the equator. Islands in the Caribbean Sea are are also part of North America. South America is the fourth largest continent. From equatorial Colombia, it extends farther south than any continent except Antarctica.

LEARN ABOUT NORTH AND SOUTH AMERICA AS YOU LOOK FOR THESE FUN ITEMS:

- ☐ Banana
- ☐ Cactuses (2)
- ☐ Coffeepot
- ☐ Igloo
- ☐ Monkey
- ☐ Moose
- ☐ Parrot
- ☐ Penguin
- ☐ Periscope
- ☐ Sailboats (2)
- ☐ Shipwreck
- ☐ Snowman
- ☐ Soccer player
- ☐ Surfer
- ☐ Swordfish

NEWFOUNDLAND

ST. JOHN'S

CHARLOTTETOWN

THIS IS PORPOISE TERRITORY!

NOVA SCOTIA

HALIFAX

ATLANTIC OCEAN

NEW BRUNSWICK

PRINCE EDWARD ISLAND

FREDERICTON

THE FRENCH AND BRITISH SETTLED THE AREA IN THE 17TH CENTURY.

GULF OF ST. LAWRENCE

CANADA IS THE WORLD'S THIRD LARGEST COUNTRY IN LAND AREA, BUT HAS ONLY 33,400,000 PEOPLE.

ST. LAWRENCE RIVER

THE PAPER BUSINESS BEGAN IN 1803 IN A SMALL PAPER MILL HERE.

PAPER PRODUCER

IRON ORE

THIS IS THE OLDEST CITY IN CANADA.

QUEBEC

MANY TOURISTS VISIT HERE.

MONTREAL IS THE SECOND LARGEST FRENCH-SPEAKING CITY IN THE WORLD.

MUCH OF QUEBEC STILL RETAINS STRONG FRENCH INFLUENCE.

THIS IS THE LARGEST PROVINCE.

A BLACK BEAR!

THE FIRST PERMANENT SETTLEMENT HERE WAS FOUNDED IN THE CITY OF QUEBEC BY SAMUEL CHAMPLAIN IN 1608.

OTTAWA IS THE CAPITAL OF CANADA.

CN TOWER

TORONTO

LAKE ONTARIO

QUEBEC

JAMES BAY

GEORGIAN BAY

LAKE HURON

FOREST PRODUCTS

LAKE ERIE

LAKE MICHIGAN

ONTARIO

ICE HOCKEY WAS INVENTED IN CANADA IN THE MID 1800S.

THAT LOOKS LIKE FUN!

THERE WERE SOMETIMES AS MANY AS 2,000 PLAYERS ON THE FIELD!

ONTARIO'S INDIANS USED TO PLAY A GAME CALLED BAGATTA, A FORERUNNER OF MODERN LACROSSE.

COPPER

LAKE SUPERIOR

UNITED STATES

NORTH

EAST

WEST

SOUTH

LEARN ABOUT THIS AREA AS YOU LOOK FOR THESE FUN ITEMS:

Canada is divided into ten provinces and three territories. Some of the eastern provinces were the first colonies to unite and form the Dominion of Canada. They had been the first areas in what is now Canada to be explored by Europeans.

- ☐ Bear
- ☐ Beaver
- ☐ Beluga whale
- ☐ Boats (2)
- ☐ Caribou
- ☐ Goose
- ☐ Hockey puck
- ☐ Moose
- ☐ Porpoise
- ☐ Snowman
- ☐ Viking

The vast regions of northern and western Canada are sparsely populated. The central plains provide fertile fields for grain production and cattle ranching. The mountainous west and forested north are rich in minerals, vegetation, and wildlife.
Nunavut, Canada's newest territory, was created in 1999. It is the traditional homeland of the Inuit (*IN-yuh-wut*) people, also known as Eskimos.

LEARN ABOUT CENTRAL AND WESTERN CANADA AS YOU LOOK FOR THESE FUN ITEMS:

- ☐ Automobile
- ☐ Beaver
- ☐ Bird
- ☐ Bucking bronco
- ☐ Buffalo
- ☐ Fisherman
- ☐ Grizzly bear
- ☐ Icebreaker
- ☐ Igloo
- ☐ Moose
- ☐ Mule deer
- ☐ Skier

THE UNITED STATES OF AMERICA

The United States of America is the world's third-largest country in population (after China and India) and the fourth-largest in land area (after Russia, China, and Canada). Its huge economic, political, and military influence make it the world's leading superpower.

In the 18th century, Britain ruled 13 American colonies. The U.S. became an independent nation in 1776, when it rebelled against British rule. Those colonies became the original 13 states. Today, the U.S. is a nation of 50 states. Washington, D.C., is the national capital and federal district. Outlying territories and other areas include Puerto Rico, the U.S. Virgin Islands, and Guam.

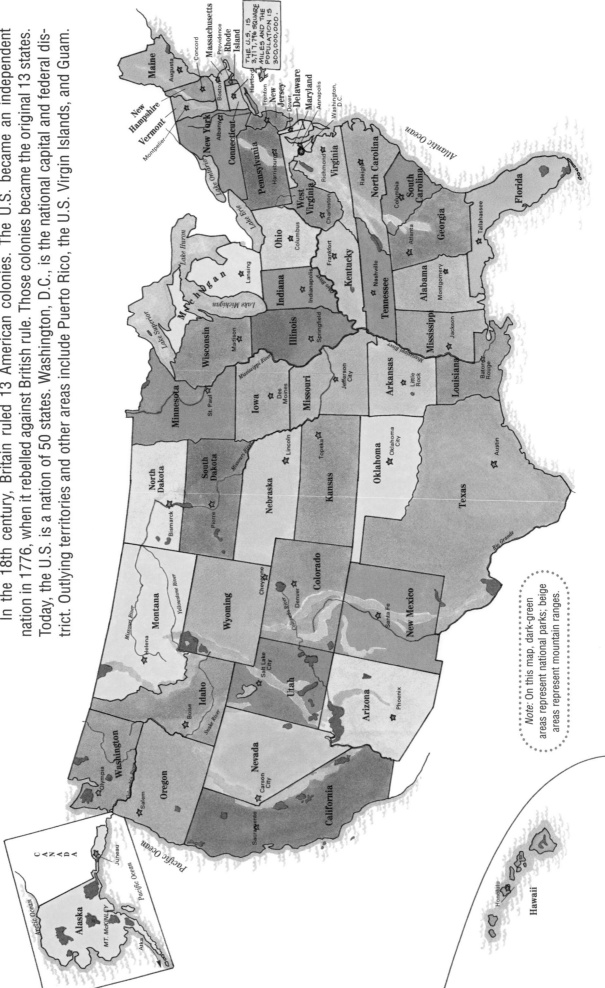

Note: On this map, dark-green areas represent national parks; beige areas represent mountain ranges.

THE U.S. IS 3,717,796 SQUARE MILES AND THE POPULATION IS 300,000,000.

In North America's far northwestern corner lies Alaska, the largest state in the U.S. In 1867, William H. Seward, the U.S. Secretary of State, bought the land from Russia for about two cents per acre. Many Americans, seeing it as a waste of money, called Alaska "Seward's Folly." Since then, however, Alaska has provided the U.S. with billions of dollars' worth of products, including oil, wood, fur, and fish.

LEARN ABOUT ALASKA AS YOU LOOK FOR THESE FUN ITEMS:

- ☐ Bald eagle
- ☐ Iceberg
- ☐ Igloo
- ☐ Log cabin
- ☐ Seal
- ☐ Snowmobile
- ☐ Sun
- ☐ Whale

THE U.S.: THE WESTERN STATES

The western part of the country is characterized by deserts, mountains, river canyons, and great forests. Separated from the rest of the continental U.S. by the Rocky Mountains, parts of this area—especially along the coast—were rapidly settled and developed after railroads were built in the mid-19th century, linking west to east.

The Hawaiian Islands became a U.S. territory in 1900 and the 50th state in 1959.

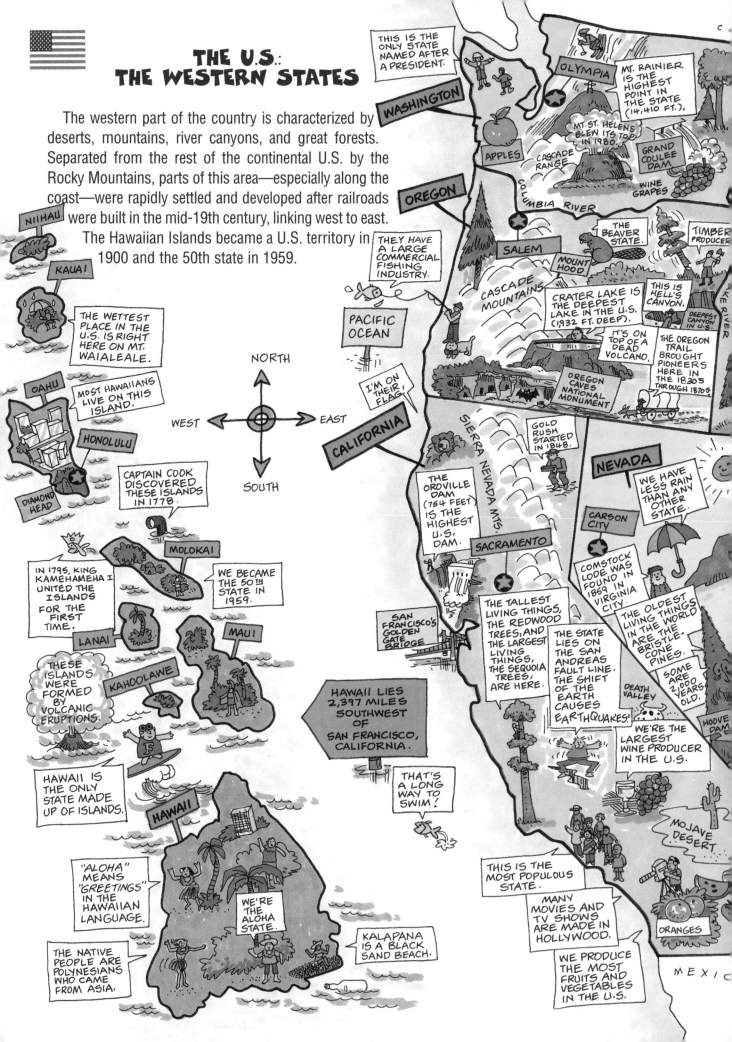

THIS IS THE ONLY STATE NAMED AFTER A PRESIDENT.

OLYMPIA

MT. RAINIER IS THE HIGHEST POINT IN THE STATE (14,410 FT.).

WASHINGTON

MT. ST. HELENS BLEW ITS TOP IN 1980.

GRAND COULEE DAM

APPLES

CASCADE RANGE

COLUMBIA RIVER

WINE GRAPES

OREGON

THE BEAVER STATE.

TIMBER PRODUCER

NIIHAU

SALEM

MOUNT HOOD

THEY HAVE A LARGE COMMERCIAL FISHING INDUSTRY.

KAUAI

THE WETTEST PLACE IN THE U.S. IS RIGHT HERE ON MT. WAIALEALE.

CASCADE MOUNTAINS

CRATER LAKE IS THE DEEPEST LAKE IN THE U.S. (1,932 FT. DEEP).

THIS IS HELL'S CANYON.

DEEPEST CANYON IN U.S.

PACIFIC OCEAN

IT'S ON TOP OF A DEAD VOLCANO.

THE OREGON TRAIL BROUGHT PIONEERS HERE IN THE 1830s THROUGH 1870s.

OREGON CAVES NATIONAL MONUMENT

OAHU

MOST HAWAIIANS LIVE ON THIS ISLAND.

NORTH
WEST EAST
SOUTH

I'M ON THEIR FLAG!

HONOLULU

CALIFORNIA

GOLD RUSH STARTED IN 1848.

NEVADA

WE HAVE LESS RAIN THAN ANY OTHER STATE.

DIAMOND HEAD

CAPTAIN COOK DISCOVERED THESE ISLANDS IN 1778.

THE OROVILLE DAM (754 FEET) IS THE HIGHEST U.S. DAM.

CARSON CITY

COMSTOCK LODE WAS FOUND IN 1869 IN VIRGINIA CITY.

SACRAMENTO

SIERRA NEVADA MTS.

THE OLDEST LIVING THINGS IN THE WORLD ARE THE BRISTLE-CONE PINES.

MOLOKAI

IN 1795, KING KAMEHAMEHA I UNITED THE ISLANDS FOR THE FIRST TIME.

WE BECAME THE 50TH STATE IN 1959.

THE TALLEST LIVING THINGS, THE REDWOOD TREES, AND THE LARGEST LIVING THINGS, THE SEQUOIA TREES, ARE HERE.

THE STATE LIES ON THE SAN ANDREAS FAULT LINE. THE SHIFT OF THE EARTH CAUSES EARTHQUAKES!

SOME ARE 2,000 YEARS OLD.

DEATH VALLEY

HOOVE DAM

LANAI

MAUI

SAN FRANCISCO'S GOLDEN GATE BRIDGE

KAHOOLAWE

THESE ISLANDS WERE FORMED BY VOLCANIC ERUPTIONS.

HAWAII LIES 2,397 MILES SOUTHWEST OF SAN FRANCISCO, CALIFORNIA.

WE'RE THE LARGEST WINE PRODUCER IN THE U.S.

HAWAII IS THE ONLY STATE MADE UP OF ISLANDS.

HAWAII

THAT'S A LONG WAY TO SWIM!

MOJAVE DESERT

"ALOHA" MEANS "GREETINGS" IN THE HAWAIIAN LANGUAGE.

WE'RE THE ALOHA STATE.

THIS IS THE MOST POPULOUS STATE.

THE NATIVE PEOPLE ARE POLYNESIANS WHO CAME FROM ASIA.

KALAPANA IS A BLACK SAND BEACH.

MANY MOVIES AND TV SHOWS ARE MADE IN HOLLYWOOD.

ORANGES

WE PRODUCE THE MOST FRUITS AND VEGETABLES IN THE U.S.

MEXICO

THE U.S.: THE MIDWESTERN STATES

Bordered by the Great Lakes to the north, the Rocky Mountains to the west, and the Appalachian Mountains to the east is a flat, fertile area known as the Great Plains. It produces more than half of the world's corn and enough wheat to make the U.S. the world's largest exporter.

LEARN ABOUT THE U.S.A.'S MIDWESTERN STATES AS YOU LOOK FOR THESE FUN ITEMS:

- ❑ Blue ox
- ❑ Book
- ❑ Cereal
- ❑ Flower
- ❑ Football
- ❑ Heart
- ❑ Race cars (3)
- ❑ Santa Claus
- ❑ Snowman
- ❑ Tire
- ❑ Watermelon slice
- ❑ Woolly mammoth

THE U.S.:
THE NORTHEASTERN AND MIDATLANTIC STATES

The most populous region in the country, the northeast and midatlantic states were the first to be settled by Europeans. Colonists arrived from England in 1620 and settled in New Plymouth, Massachusetts.

LEARN ABOUT U.S.A.'S NORTHEASTERN AND MIDATLANTIC STATES AS YOU LOOK FOR THESE FUN ITEMS:

- ❏ Anchor
- ❏ Apple
- ❏ Baseball
- ❏ Basketball
- ❏ Cannon
- ❏ Kite
- ❏ Lighthouse
- ❏ Lobster
- ❏ Ship
- ❏ Skier
- ❏ Treasure chest
- ❏ Truck
- ❏ Umbrella

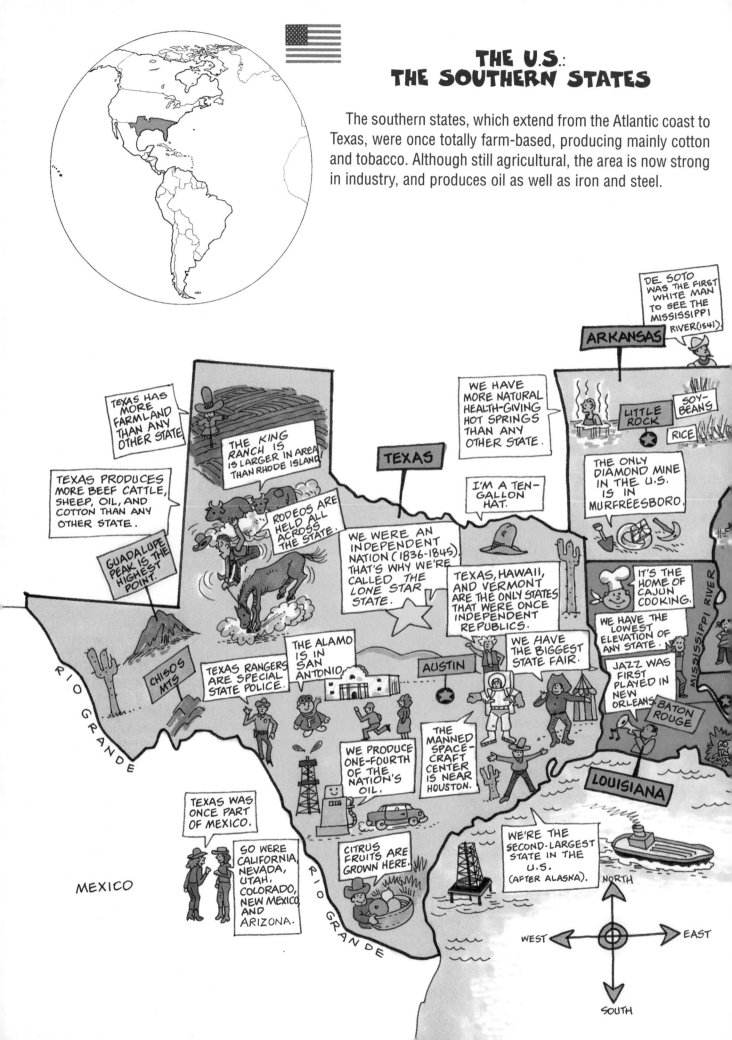

THE U.S.: THE SOUTHERN STATES

The southern states, which extend from the Atlantic coast to Texas, were once totally farm-based, producing mainly cotton and tobacco. Although still agricultural, the area is now strong in industry, and produces oil as well as iron and steel.

MEXICO AND CENTRAL AMERICA

The peoples of Mexico and Central America are mostly of Spanish or Indian ancestry, or a mixture of both. Mexico, a hot and dry region of North America, is rich in precious metals and petroleum. The seven countries of Central America are mainly agricultural. Dotted with active volcanoes, the land has jungles and high mountains, and the climate is hot and steamy, perfect for growing coffee, bananas, and other tropical crops.

LEARN ABOUT MEXICO, CENTRAL AMERICA, AND THE CARIBBEAN NATIONS AS YOU LOOK FOR THESE FUN ITEMS:

- ❑ Armadillo
- ❑ Coffeepots (3)
- ❑ Cotton (3)
- ❑ Diver
- ❑ Miner
- ❑ Oil well
- ❑ Photographer
- ❑ Pineapple
- ❑ Sailor
- ❑ Scarecrow
- ❑ Shovel
- ❑ Shrimp (3)
- ❑ Squash
- ❑ Turtle
- ❑ Umbrellas (3)

THE CARIBBEAN NATIONS

A chain of tropical islands about 2,000 miles long stretches across the Caribbean Sea, then curves like a hook toward South America. These islands were the first land in the Americas that Christopher Columbus saw and set foot on during his 1492 voyage of discovery. In the 16th century, Europeans colonized the islands, bringing African slaves to work plantations.

Today, 13 of the islands or island groups are independent nations (see list below). Others are territories of the U.S. or European countries. Most of the people living here are descendants of African slaves, Spanish conquerors, or both. Most countries in this region depend on tourism and agriculture for their income.

COUNTRY NAME ✹CAPITAL CITY	POPULATION	LANGUAGE
ANTIGUA & BARBUDA ✹ST. JOHN'S	69,000	ENGLISH
BAHAMAS ✹NASSAU	304,000	ENGLISH
BARBADOS ✹BRIDGETOWN	280,000	ENGLISH
CUBA ✹HAVANA	11,300,000	SPANISH
DOMINICA ✹ROSEAU	70,000	ENGLISH
DOMINICAN REPUBLIC ✹SANTO DOMINGO	9,200,000	SPANISH
GRENADA ✹ST. GEORGE'S	90,000	ENGLISH
HAITI ✹PORT-AU-PRINCE	8,500,000	HAITIAN CREOLE AND FRENCH
JAMAICA ✹KINGSTON	2,800,000	ENGLISH
SAINT KITTS ✹NEVIS ✹BASSETERRE	40,000	ENGLISH
SAINT LUCIA ✹CASTRIES	168,000	ENGLISH
SAINT VINCENT & THE GRENADINES ✹KINGSTOWN	118,000	ENGLISH
TRINIDAD & TOBAGO ✹PORT-OF-SPAIN	1,100,000	ENGLISH

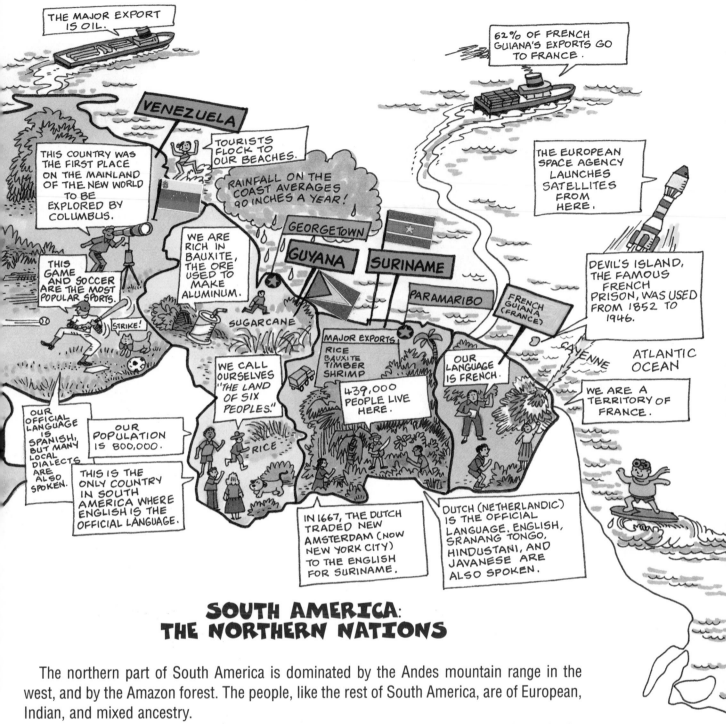

SOUTH AMERICA: THE NORTHERN NATIONS

The northern part of South America is dominated by the Andes mountain range in the west, and by the Amazon forest. The people, like the rest of South America, are of European, Indian, and mixed ancestry.

Once Spanish colonies, Ecuador, Colombia, and Venezuela won their independence in the early decades of the 19th century. Guyana and Suriname gained their independence only recently: Guyana in 1966, from Britain; and Suriname in 1975, from the Netherlands. French Guiana is the only country on the South American mainland that is still a European territory.

LEARN ABOUT SOUTH AMERICA'S NORTHERN NATIONS AS YOU LOOK FOR THESE FUN ITEMS:

- ❏ Aluminum can
- ❏ Angel
- ❏ Baseball bat
- ❏ Cup
- ❏ Emerald
- ❏ Flying bat
- ❏ Ibis
- ❏ Iguana
- ❏ Jaguar
- ❏ Mountain climber
- ❏ Photographer
- ❏ Satellite rocket
- ❏ Schoolteacher
- ❏ Soccer ball
- ❏ Stone idol
- ❏ Surfer
- ❏ Telescope
- ❏ Turtle

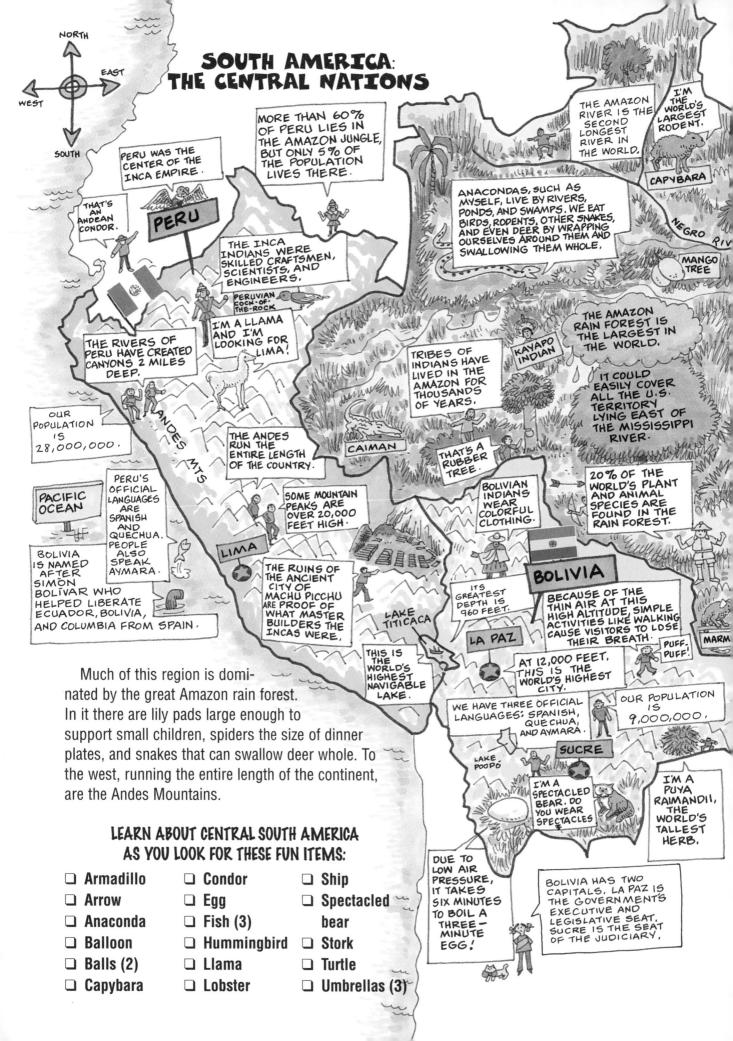

SOUTH AMERICA: THE CENTRAL NATIONS

NORTH
EAST
WEST
SOUTH

PERU WAS THE CENTER OF THE INCA EMPIRE.

MORE THAN 60% OF PERU LIES IN THE AMAZON JUNGLE, BUT ONLY 5% OF THE POPULATION LIVES THERE.

THE AMAZON RIVER IS THE SECOND LONGEST RIVER IN THE WORLD.

I'M THE WORLD'S LARGEST RODENT.

THAT'S AN ANDEAN CONDOR.

PERU

THE INCA INDIANS WERE SKILLED CRAFTSMEN, SCIENTISTS, AND ENGINEERS.

ANACONDAS, SUCH AS MYSELF, LIVE BY RIVERS, PONDS, AND SWAMPS. WE EAT BIRDS, RODENTS, OTHER SNAKES, AND EVEN DEER BY WRAPPING OURSELVES AROUND THEM AND SWALLOWING THEM WHOLE.

CAPYBARA

NEGRO RIV

MANGO TREE

PERUVIAN COCK-OF-THE-ROCK

I'M A LLAMA AND I'M LOOKING FOR LIMA!

THE RIVERS OF PERU HAVE CREATED CANYONS 2 MILES DEEP.

TRIBES OF INDIANS HAVE LIVED IN THE AMAZON FOR THOUSANDS OF YEARS.

KAYAPO INDIAN

THE AMAZON RAIN FOREST IS THE LARGEST IN THE WORLD.

IT COULD EASILY COVER ALL THE U.S. TERRITORY LYING EAST OF THE MISSISSIPPI RIVER.

OUR POPULATION IS 28,000,000.

THE ANDES RUN THE ENTIRE LENGTH OF THE COUNTRY.

CAIMAN

THAT'S A RUBBER TREE.

PERU'S OFFICIAL LANGUAGES ARE SPANISH AND QUECHUA. PEOPLE ALSO SPEAK AYMARA.

PACIFIC OCEAN

SOME MOUNTAIN PEAKS ARE OVER 20,000 FEET HIGH.

BOLIVIAN INDIANS WEAR COLORFUL CLOTHING.

20% OF THE WORLD'S PLANT AND ANIMAL SPECIES ARE FOUND IN THE RAIN FOREST.

BOLIVIA

BOLIVIA IS NAMED AFTER SIMÓN BOLÍVAR WHO HELPED LIBERATE ECUADOR, BOLIVIA, AND COLUMBIA FROM SPAIN.

LIMA

THE RUINS OF THE ANCIENT CITY OF MACHU PICCHU ARE PROOF OF WHAT MASTER BUILDERS THE INCAS WERE.

ITS GREATEST DEPTH IS 960 FEET.

BECAUSE OF THE THIN AIR AT THIS HIGH ALTITUDE, SIMPLE ACTIVITIES LIKE WALKING CAUSE VISITORS TO LOSE THEIR BREATH.

PUFF, PUFF!

MARM

LAKE TITICACA

LA PAZ

THIS IS THE WORLD'S HIGHEST NAVIGABLE LAKE.

AT 12,000 FEET, THIS IS THE WORLD'S HIGHEST CITY.

Much of this region is dominated by the great Amazon rain forest. In it there are lily pads large enough to support small children, spiders the size of dinner plates, and snakes that can swallow deer whole. To the west, running the entire length of the continent, are the Andes Mountains.

WE HAVE THREE OFFICIAL LANGUAGES: SPANISH, QUECHUA, AND AYMARA.

OUR POPULATION IS 9,000,000.

LAKE POOPÓ

SUCRE

I'M A SPECTACLED BEAR. DO YOU WEAR SPECTACLES?

I'M A PUYA RAIMANDII, THE WORLD'S TALLEST HERB.

LEARN ABOUT CENTRAL SOUTH AMERICA AS YOU LOOK FOR THESE FUN ITEMS:

- ☐ Armadillo
- ☐ Arrow
- ☐ Anaconda
- ☐ Balloon
- ☐ Balls (2)
- ☐ Capybara
- ☐ Condor
- ☐ Egg
- ☐ Fish (3)
- ☐ Hummingbird
- ☐ Llama
- ☐ Lobster
- ☐ Ship
- ☐ Spectacled bear
- ☐ Stork
- ☐ Turtle
- ☐ Umbrellas (3)

DUE TO LOW AIR PRESSURE, IT TAKES SIX MINUTES TO BOIL A THREE-MINUTE EGG!

BOLIVIA HAS TWO CAPITALS. LA PAZ IS THE GOVERNMENT'S EXECUTIVE AND LEGISLATIVE SEAT. SUCRE IS THE SEAT OF THE JUDICIARY.

SOUTH AMERICA: THE SOUTHERN NATIONS

The southern region of South America has various types of landscapes, including grassy plains, deserts, mountains, forests, and frozen glaciers. It is a region rich in natural resources.

LEARN ABOUT SOUTH AMERICA'S SOUTHERN NATIONS AS YOU LOOK FOR THESE FUN ITEMS:

- ☐ Albatross
- ☐ Anteater
- ☐ Ball
- ☐ Boat
- ☐ Dancers
- ☐ Grapes

- ☐ Hairy armadillo
- ☐ Heart
- ☐ Oil wells (2)
- ☐ Penguins (2)
- ☐ Seal
- ☐ Skier
- ☐ Snowman
- ☐ Trout
- ☐ Umbrellas (2)
- ☐ Volcanoes (2)

EUROPE

The seat of Western civilization, Europe has had a strong influence on the world through trade, exploration, and industry.

The continent stretches from the icy Arctic Circle in the north to the warm Mediterranean Sea in the south. Its western border is the North Atlantic Ocean and its eastern borders are the Ural and Caucasus mountains. The land—with its fertile plains and tall mountains—is as varied as its countries, peoples, and cultures.

LEARN ABOUT EUROPE AS YOU LOOK FOR THESE FUN ITEMS:

- ☐ Cyclist
- ☐ Eiffel Tower
- ☐ Fish (3)
- ☐ Grapes
- ☐ Puffin
- ☐ Sailboat
- ☐ Volcano
- ☐ Windmill
- ☐ Wooden shoe

FINLAND

RUSSIA

LAKE LADOGA

ESTONIA

LATVIA

LITHUANIA

BELARUS

FLAX

SUGAR BEETS

UKRAINE

MOLDOVA

WHEAT

DNIEPER RV.

DON RIVER

ROMANIA

TRANSYLVANIAN ALPS

BULGARIA

TURKEY

AEGEAN SEA

VOLGA RIVER

THE VOLGA (RUNNING FOR 2,290 MILES) IS THE LONGEST RIVER IN EUROPE.

EUROPE IS CONSIDERED THE BIRTHPLACE OF WESTERN CIVILIZATION.

CASPIAN SEA

CAUCASUS MTS

THE HIGHEST POINT IN EUROPE IS MT. ELBRUS IN THE CAUCASUS RANGE IN RUSSIA.

THE DANUBE RIVER FLOWS THROUGH 7 EUROPEAN COUNTRIES.

THE BLACK SEA

NORTH
EAST
WEST
SOUTH

EUROPE IS THE WORLD'S SECOND SMALLEST CONTINENT (ONLY AUSTRALIA IS SMALLER). YET IT RANKS THIRD IN POPULATION, AFTER ASIA AND AFRICA.

EUROPE HAS AN AREA OF ABOUT 4,000,000 SQUARE MILES.

ITS POPULATION IS 730,000,000.

THE LARGEST LAKE IN EUROPE IS LADOGA, IN RUSSIA (7,000 SQ. MILES).

UNITED KINGDOM AND IRELAND

The United Kingdom is a country made up of four parts: England, Wales, Scotland, and Northern Ireland. (The first three are also known as Britain.) Northern Ireland is on the same large island as the independent country of Ireland. In the late 19th and early 20th centuries, Great Britain was the world's leading industrial and trading nation. Its worldwide empire included Canada, India, Australia, New Zealand, and parts of Africa.

LEARN ABOUT THE UNITED KINGDOM AND IRELAND AS YOU LOOK FOR THESE FUN ITEMS:

☐ Bagpipe
☐ Big Ben
☐ Bus
☐ Deer
☐ Ferry
☐ Four-leaf clover
☐ Golf
☐ Knight in armor
☐ Lobster
☐ "Nessie"
☐ Sheep (3)
☐ Soccer ball
☐ Tennis racket

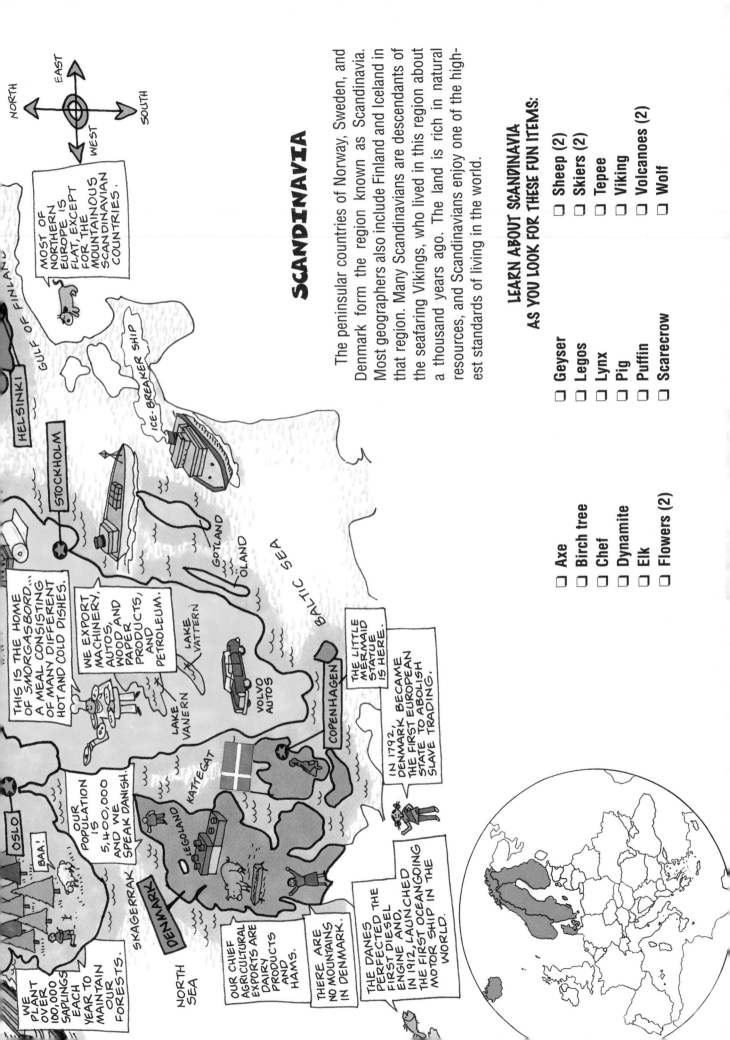

SCANDINAVIA

The peninsular countries of Norway, Sweden, and Denmark form the region known as Scandinavia. Most geographers also include Finland and Iceland in that region. Many Scandinavians are descendants of the seafaring Vikings, who lived in this region about a thousand years ago. The land is rich in natural resources, and Scandinavians enjoy one of the highest standards of living in the world.

LEARN ABOUT SCANDINAVIA AS YOU LOOK FOR THESE FUN ITEMS:

- ☐ Axe
- ☐ Birch tree
- ☐ Chef
- ☐ Dynamite
- ☐ Elk
- ☐ Flowers (2)

- ☐ Geyser
- ☐ Legos
- ☐ Lynx
- ☐ Pig
- ☐ Puffin
- ☐ Scarecrow

- ☐ Sheep (2)
- ☐ Skiers (2)
- ☐ Tepee
- ☐ Viking
- ☐ Volcanoes (2)
- ☐ Wolf

THE BALTIC NATIONS AND EUROPEAN RUSSIA

Before 1991, the countries in this region were part of the vast Soviet Union—also called the Union of Soviet Socialist Republics, or U.S.S.R. In 1991, that vast country broke apart, and now Estonia, Latvia, Lithuania, Belarus, Ukraine, and Moldova are independent countries. They are called "Baltic nations" because they were in the part of the Soviet Union that lay west of Russia and on or near the Baltic Sea.

Most of Russia is in Asia, but the part west of the Ural Mountains—which includes the capital city—is part of Europe.

LEARN ABOUT THE BALTIC NATIONS AND EUROPEAN RUSSIA AS YOU LOOK FOR THESE FUN ITEMS:

- ❑ Ballet dancers
- ❑ Bus
- ❑ Camera
- ❑ Chess piece
- ❑ Duck
- ❑ Elk
- ❑ European bison
- ❑ Frame
- ❑ Mouse
- ❑ Rabbit
- ❑ Scarecrow
- ❑ Shovel
- ❑ Trucks (3)
- ❑ Seals (2)
- ❑ Ships (3)
- ❑ Statue
- ❑ Turtle
- ❑ Wolves (2)

THE CITY OF GDANSK, ON THE BALTIC SEA, HAS MAJOR SHIP-BUILDING FACILITIES.

BALTIC SEA

POLAND

SHIP BUILDING

POTATOES AND GRAINS ARE THE MAJOR CROPS.

LOTS OF US ARE RAISED HERE.

DEEP WOODS COVER 1/4 OF POLAND.

NEARLY 1/3 OF THE LABOR FORCE WORKS IN AGRICULTURE.

GDANSK

MASURIAN LAKES

POLAND REACHED ITS PEAK OF POWER BETWEEN THE 14TH AND 17TH CENTURIES.

OUR POPULATION IS 38,600,000 AND WE SPEAK POLISH.

HAVING FEW NATURAL BOUNDARIES, POLAND HAS BEEN INVADED FROM BOTH EAST AND WEST AND HAS AT TIMES NOT EXISTED AS A SEPARATE COUNTRY.

WOODEN WINDMILLS

ONE NATIONAL PARK IN POLAND HAS MORE THAN 1,800 SPECIES OF BUTTERFLIES.

ONE AREA IN POLAND HAS 485 SQUARE MILES OF THE LAST REMAINING LOWLAND PRIMEVAL FOREST IN CENTRAL EUROPE.

VISTULA RIVER

WARSAW

SETTLED IN THE 11TH CENTURY, WARSAW IS KNOWN FOR ITS THEATER, MUSIC, AND ART.

POPULAR FOODS ARE KIELBASA (SPICY SAUSAGE) AND HAM.

WE ARE RICH IN COAL, NATURAL GAS, SULPHUR, AND COPPER.

INDUSTRY HERE INCLUDES MACHINERY, TEXTILES, IRON, STEEL, AND CHEMICALS.

CZECH REPUBLIC

ELBE RV.

PRAGUE

SUGAR BEETS

CHAMOIS (SMALL GOAT-LIKE ANTELOPE), BEARS, LYNX, WOLVES, EAGLES, AND BLACK STORKS LIVE HERE.

THE CITY OF KRAKOW HAS MANY BEAUTIFUL HISTORIC BUILDINGS.

VISTULA RIVER

BAA!

CARPATHIAN MTS

BOHEMIA, IN THE WEST, IS A PLATEAU SURROUNDED BY FORESTS AND LOW MOUNTAINS.

WE HAVE COAL, TIMBER, AND URANIUM.

THE HILLY LAND OF MORAVIA IS AN IMPORTANT FARMING AREA.

VLTAVA RIVER

OUR POPULATION IS 10,300,000 AND OUR LANGUAGE IS CZECH.

ALMOST 50% OF OUR COUNTRY CONSISTS OF MOUNTAINS, FORESTS, AND PASTURES.

NORTH
WEST
EAST
SOUTH

THIS HEAVILY INDUSTRIALIZED COUNTRY PRODUCES AUTOS, MACHINERY, CHEMICALS, ELECTRONICS AND MANY OTHER MANUFACTURED ITEMS.

SLOVAKIA

BRATISLAVA

BARLEY, SUGAR BEETS, PAPRIKA, AND MELONS ARE MAJOR AGRICULTURAL PRODUCTS.

METAL PROCESSING

RED PAPRIKA IS THE NATIONAL SPICE.

MT. KÉKES (3,330 FT)

HUNGARY

BUDAPEST

AFTER BEING RULED BY THE AUSTRIAN EMPIRE FOR 300 YEARS, CZECH LANDS AND SLOVAKIA WERE UNITED TO FORM CZECHOSLOVAKIA IN 1918.

LAKE BALATON IS THE LARGEST LAKE IN CENTRAL EUROPE.

PARLIAMENT BUILDINGS

CZECHOSLOVAKIA SPLIT PEACEFULLY INTO THE CZECH REPUBLIC AND SLOVAKIA ON JANUARY 1, 1993.

CHICKEN PAPRIKA IS ONE OF OUR FAMOUS DISHES.

PIANIST AND COMPOSER FRANZ LISZT WAS HUNGARIAN. HE CREATED THE SYMPHONIC POEM.

DANUBE RIVER

POLAND, CZECH REPUBLIC, SLOVAKIA, AND HUNGARY

When World War II ended in 1945, many countries in Eastern Europe came under the control of the Soviet Union. When the Soviet Union broke apart in 1991, the people in Poland, Czechoslovakia, and Hungary once again took charge of their own governments. In 1993, Czechoslovakia split into two independent countries, the Czech Republic and Slovakia.

LEARN ABOUT POLAND, CZECH REPUBLC, SLOVAKIA, AND HUNGARY AS YOU LOOK FOR THESE FUN ITEMS:

❏ Barn
❏ Bear
❏ Bird
❏ Bison
❏ Butterflies (4)
❏ Carrot
❏ Cooks (3)
❏ Flower
❏ Hockey player
❏ Music notes

❏ Pigs (2)
❏ Radio tower
❏ Sausage
❏ Scarecrows (5)
❏ Sheep
❏ Tennis ball
❏ Tourists
❏ Truck
❏ Windmill
❏ Woolly mammoth

THE NORTHEASTERN REGION IS DENSE WITH TALL TREES AND LAKES.

BUG RIVER

EUROPEAN BISON

PALACE OF CULTURE

OJCOW NATIONAL PARK IN THE SOUTH HAS 50 CAVES WHERE PREHISTORIC PEOPLE LIVED.

REMAINS OF PREHISTORIC MAMMOTHS HAVE ALSO BEEN FOUND THERE.

OUR POPULATION IS 5,400,000 AND OUR LANGUAGES ARE SLOVAK AND HUNGARIAN.

GOULASH, A TRADITIONAL HUNGARIAN DISH, IS A STEW OF MEAT, POTATOES, ONIONS, AND PAPRIKA (A SPICE MADE FROM SWEET RED PEPPERS), AND IS MY FAVORITE DISH TO MAKE.

WE'RE NOT LOST!

BECAUSE MOST OF OUR LAND IS FERTILE, HUNGARIANS PRODUCE ENOUGH FOOD TO FEED THE COUNTRY AND SELL ABROAD.

OUR POPULATION IS 10,100,000.

GERMANY, SWITZERLAND, LIECHTENSTEIN, AND AUSTRIA

BALTIC SEA

The countries of Germany, Switzerland, Liechtenstein, and Austria lie in an area sometimes known as central Europe. From north to south, this region's landscape changes from marshy plains to snowcapped moutains. It is crossed by two of Europe's longest rivers—the Rhine and the Danube—and by the Alps, the famous mountain range that is the longest and highest mountain range in western Europe.

LEARN ABOUT GERMANY, SWITZERLAND, LIECHTENSTEIN, AND AUSTRIA AS YOU LOOK FOR THESE FUN ITEMS:

- ❏ Alpine horn blower
- ❏ Automobiles (3)
- ❏ Axe
- ❏ Berlin Wall
- ❏ Books (3)
- ❏ Cake
- ❏ Carrot
- ❏ Chicken
- ❏ Coal miner
- ❏ Cookies
- ❏ Cows (2)
- ❏ Cuckoo clock
- ❏ Dogs (2)
- ❏ Great white heron
- ❏ Horse
- ❏ Hot dogs
- ❏ Pigs (2)
- ❏ Soccer ball
- ❏ Telescope
- ❏ Tuba
- ❏ Watch

TEXTILES

HISTORICALLY, THE LAND OF GERMANY HAS BEEN MORE DIVIDED THAN UNITED, CONSISTING OF SMALL INDEPENDENT STATES.

AFTER GERMANY WAS DEFEATED IN WORLD WAR II, THE COUNTRY WAS DIVIDED INTO EAST AND WEST GERMANY. BERLIN WAS DIVIDED BY A CONCRETE WALL IN 1961. TODAY, GERMANY IS UNITED.

GERMANY IS ONE OF THE WORLD'S MOST INDUSTRIALIZED COUNTRIES. WE EXPORT AUTOS, MACHINES, CHEMICALS, ELECTRONICS, AND IRON AND STEEL PRODUCTS.

AUSTRIA

VIENNA OPERA HOUSE

WE ARE FAMOUS FOR OUR TRADITIONAL MUSIC.

VIENNA

OUR POPULATION IS 8,100,000 AND WE SPEAK GERMAN.

WOLFGANG AMADEUS MOZART WAS BORN IN SALZBURG, AUSTRIA, IN 1756.

THE WORLD-FAMOUS LIPIZZANER HORSES COME FROM AUSTRIA.

I'M A GREAT WHITE HERON FROM AUSTRIA.

ABOUT 3/4 OF THE COUNTRY IS COVERED BY THE ALPS.

THE HIGHEST PEAK IN AUSTRIA IS THE GROSSGLOCKNER (GREAT BELL), AT 12,461 FEET.

LIECHTENSTEIN WAS FOUNDED IN 1719 AND IS ABOUT THE SIZE OF WASHINGTON, D.C.

THE RHINE VALLEY COVERS 1/3 OF THE COUNTRY AND THE ALPS COVER THE REST.

LIECHTENSTEIN IS IN AN ECONOMIC UNION WITH SWITZERLAND. FOR MORE THAN 100 YEARS, THE COUNTRY HAS HAD NO ARMY, ONLY LOCAL POLICE.

THE NETHERLANDS, BELGIUM, AND LUXEMBOURG

The Netherlands is situated on very low-lying land. With an average altitude of only 37 feet, it is the flattest country in the world! (The word *Netherlands* means "the lowlands.") Belgium, though not as flat, also sits low. The two lands are known as "the Low Countries."

Those two countries plus Luxembourg are sometimes referred to as "Benelux." Their small size and large populations make this region one of the most densely populated areas in Europe.

LEARN ABOUT THE NETHERLANDS, BELGIUM, AND LUXEMBOURG AS YOU LOOK FOR THESE FUN ITEMS:

- ☐ Crystal
- ☐ Deer
- ☐ Diamonds (2)
- ☐ Fishing pole
- ☐ Frame
- ☐ Grapes
- ☐ Pig
- ☐ Santa Claus
- ☐ Shovel
- ☐ Soccer ball
- ☐ Telescope
- ☐ Tulips (5)
- ☐ TV set
- ☐ Waffle
- ☐ Windmills (5)
- ☐ Wooden shoes (2 pairs)

FRANCE AND MONACO

France is one of the oldest countries in Europe. It also is one of the world's leading countries in terms of culture, historic and political influence, industry, and agriculture. The capital and cultural center is the city of Paris, nicknamed "the City of Light."

At France's southeastern corner lies Monaco, one of the world's smallest nations. (*Monaco* is also the name of its capital city.)

LEARN ABOUT FRANCE AND MONACO AS YOU LOOK FOR THESE FUN ITEMS:

- ❏ Apples (2)
- ❏ Artichoke
- ❏ Artist
- ❏ Automobile
- ❏ Chef
- ❏ Cyclist
- ❏ Dice
- ❏ Eels
- ❏ Eiffel Tower
- ❏ Geese (2)
- ❏ Mouse
- ❏ Musician
- ❏ Mustard
- ❏ Napoleon
- ❏ Paper airplane
- ❏ Perfume bottle
- ❏ Pig
- ❏ Red balloon
- ❏ Skier
- ❏ Snail
- ❏ Soccer ball
- ❏ Umbrellas (2)
- ❏ Walnuts

THE IBERIAN PENINSULA

Spain, Portugal, and Andorra share a piece of land called the Iberian Peninsula. (A *peninsula* is a land area with water on all sides except for a neck of land connected to a larger landmass.) Spain and Portugal have long seafaring histories. Their explorers and settlers once ruled empires in Africa, Asia, North America, and South America. Tiny Andorra, tucked into an area of the Pyrenees Mountains, is landlocked.

Today, fishing, farming, and tourism are major industries in Spain and Portugal. More than 60 million tourists each year visit their historical cities and sun-drenched beaches.

LEARN ABOUT THE IBERIAN PENINSULA AS YOU LOOK FOR THESE FUN ITEMS:

- ❑ Anchovies
- ❑ Bottles (5)
- ❑ Brown bear
- ❑ Bulls (3)
- ❑ Cheese
- ❑ Cork
- ❑ Guitar
- ❑ Ibex
- ❑ Olive tree
- ❑ Skier
- ❑ Sunflowers (4)
- ❑ Umbrellas (3)
- ❑ Windmill
- ❑ Windsurfers (3)

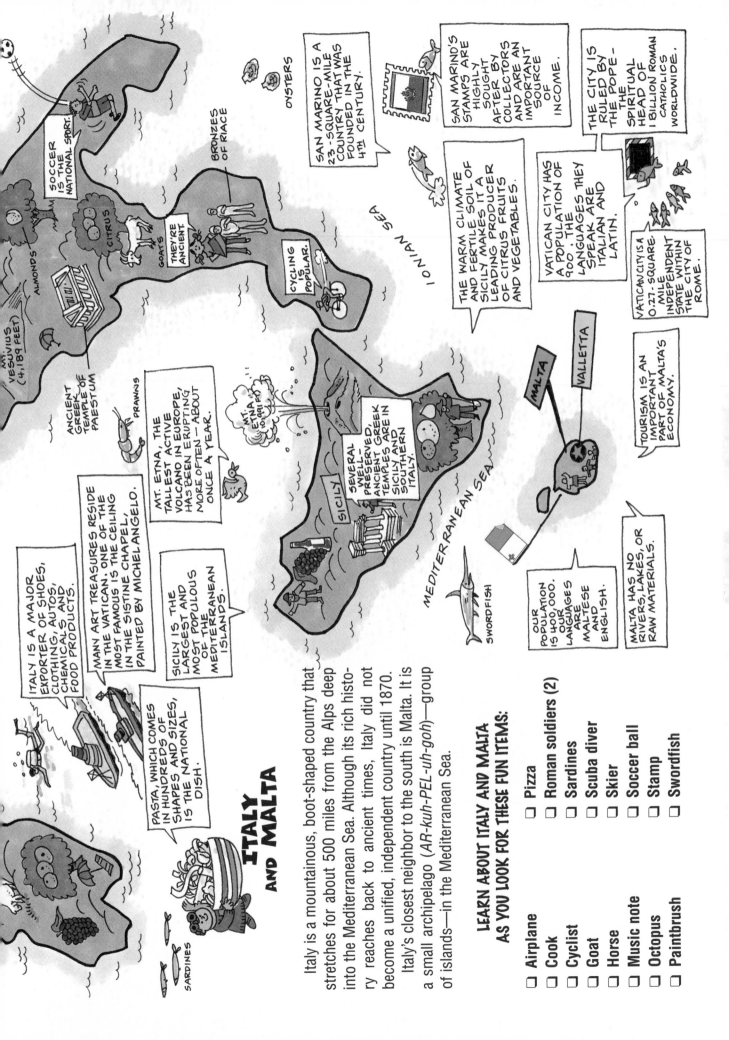

ITALY AND MALTA

Italy is a mountainous, boot-shaped country that stretches for about 500 miles from the Alps deep into the Mediterranean Sea. Although its rich history reaches back to ancient times, Italy did not become a unified, independent country until 1870. Italy's closest neighbor to the south is Malta. It is a small archipelago (*AR-kuh-PEL-uh-goh*)—group of islands—in the Mediterranean Sea.

LEARN ABOUT ITALY AND MALTA AS YOU LOOK FOR THESE FUN ITEMS:

☐ Airplane
☐ Cook
☐ Cyclist
☐ Goat
☐ Horse
☐ Music note
☐ Octopus
☐ Paintbrush
☐ Pizza
☐ Roman soldiers (2)
☐ Sardines
☐ Scuba diver
☐ Skier
☐ Soccer ball
☐ Stamp
☐ Swordfish

**Map labels:**

SOCCER IS THE NATIONAL SPORT.

CITRUS

ALMONDS

GOATS

THEY'RE ANCIENT

MT. VESUVIUS (4,189 FEET)

ANCIENT GREEK TEMPLE OF PAESTUM

BRONZES OF RIACE

CYCLING IS POPULAR.

OYSTERS

SAN MARINO IS A 23-SQUARE-MILE COUNTRY THAT WAS FOUNDED IN THE 4TH CENTURY.

SAN MARINO'S STAMPS ARE HIGHLY SOUGHT AFTER BY COLLECTORS AND ARE AN IMPORTANT SOURCE OF INCOME.

THE CITY IS RULED BY THE POPE—THE SPIRITUAL HEAD OF 1 BILLION ROMAN CATHOLICS WORLDWIDE.

THE WARM CLIMATE AND FERTILE SOIL OF SICILY MAKES IT A LEADING PRODUCER OF CITRUS FRUITS AND VEGETABLES.

VATICAN CITY HAS A POPULATION OF 900. THE LANGUAGES THEY SPEAK ARE ITALIAN AND LATIN.

VATICAN CITY IS A 0.27-SQUARE-MILE INDEPENDENT STATE WITHIN THE CITY OF ROME.

IONIAN SEA

PRAWNS

MT. ETNA, THE TALLEST ACTIVE VOLCANO IN EUROPE, HAS BEEN ERUPTING MORE OFTEN—ABOUT ONCE A YEAR.

MT. ETNA 10,991 FT.

SEVERAL WELL-PRESERVED, ANCIENT GREEK TEMPLES ARE IN SICILY AND SOUTHERN ITALY.

SICILY

MALTA

VALLETTA

MEDITERRANEAN SEA

TOURISM IS AN IMPORTANT PART OF MALTA'S ECONOMY.

SWORDFISH

OUR POPULATION IS 400,000. OUR LANGUAGES ARE MALTESE AND ENGLISH.

MALTA HAS NO RIVERS, LAKES, OR RAW MATERIALS.

ITALY IS A MAJOR EXPORTER OF SHOES, CLOTHING, AUTOS, CHEMICALS AND FOOD PRODUCTS.

MANY ART TREASURES RESIDE IN THE VATICAN, ONE OF THE MOST FAMOUS IS THE CEILING IN THE SISTINE CHAPEL, PAINTED BY MICHELANGELO.

SICILY IS THE LARGEST AND MOST POPULOUS OF THE MEDITERRANEAN ISLANDS.

PASTA, WHICH COMES IN HUNDREDS OF SHAPES AND SIZES, IS THE NATIONAL DISH.

SARDINES

THE BALKAN NATIONS

Much of this part of eastern Europe, known as the Balkans, was ruled by Turkey from the end of the 15th century until 1913. (The name *Balkan* comes from the Balkan Mountains of Bulgaria.) After World War I, several regions were combined to form Yugoslavia. It was heavily influenced by its huge neighbor, the Soviet Union. Soon after the Soviet Union broke apart in 1991, so did Yugoslavia. That land is now five independent countries: Serbia and Montenegro, Slovenia, Croatia, Bosnia and Herzegovina, and Macedonia.

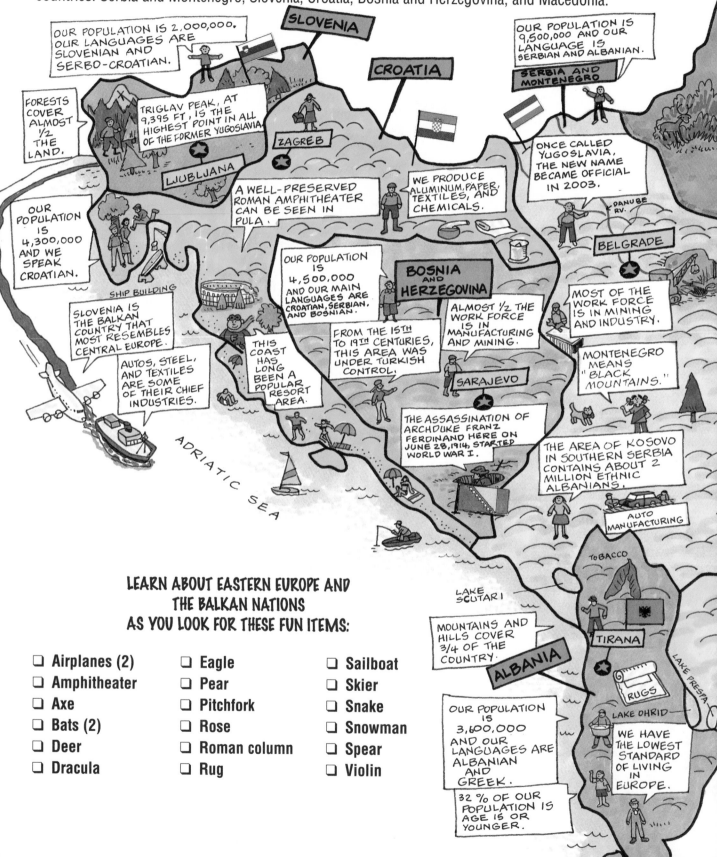

LEARN ABOUT EASTERN EUROPE AND THE BALKAN NATIONS AS YOU LOOK FOR THESE FUN ITEMS:

- ❑ Airplanes (2)
- ❑ Amphitheater
- ❑ Axe
- ❑ Bats (2)
- ❑ Deer
- ❑ Dracula
- ❑ Eagle
- ❑ Pear
- ❑ Pitchfork
- ❑ Rose
- ❑ Roman column
- ❑ Rug
- ❑ Sailboat
- ❑ Skier
- ❑ Snake
- ❑ Snowman
- ❑ Spear
- ❑ Violin

GREECE

The ideals of Western democracy were born in Greece about 2,500 years ago. The art, philosophy, theater, mythology, science, and architecture that flourished there formed the basis of Western civilization.

LEARN ABOUT GREECE AS YOU LOOK FOR THESE FUN ITEMS:
- ❏ Book
- ❏ Cotton
- ❏ Grapes
- ❏ Octopus
- ❏ Olympic torch bearer
- ❏ Sailboat
- ❏ Stone lion
- ❏ Telescope

ABOUT 80% OF GREECE IS MOUNTAINOUS.

NORTH WEST EAST SOUTH

TRADITIONAL COSTUME

OUR POPULATION IS 11,000,000 AND WE SPEAK GREEK.

SHEEP ARE THE PRIMARY LIVESTOCK IN GREECE.

BLACK SEA

TURKEY

THIS PART OF TURKEY IS IN EUROPE.

SEA OF MARMARA

GREECE

MANY TOURISTS VISIT GREECE AND ITS ISLANDS.

THEATER OF DODONA

MT. OLYMPUS (9,570 FT)

DEMOCRACY IS A GREEK WORD MEANING "POWER OF THE PEOPLE."

THE OLYMPIC GAMES WERE FIRST HELD HERE IN 776 B.C.

OLIVE OIL AND WINE ARE PRODUCED IN ABUNDANCE.

AEGEAN SEA

THE RUINS OF MANY ANCIENT TEMPLES, STATUES, AND MONUMENTS CAN STILL BE SEEN IN GREECE.

COTTON

RUINS OF DELPHI

GUARDIAN LION STATUES ON DELOS

ANCIENT GREEK VASE

LEMONS

ADRIATIC SEA

IN THE 8TH CENTURY B.C., GREEKS CREATED A NETWORK OF COLONIES ALONG THE MEDITERRANEAN COAST AS FAR AS SPAIN.

RUINS OF OLYMPIA

GREECE WAS A TURKISH PROVINCE FROM 1460 UNTIL 1827.

ROAD OF CORINTH

GREECE'S HEAVILY INDENTED COASTLINE IS 9,385 MILES LONG.

ATHENS

IONIAN SEA

ON A ROCKY HILL IN ATHENS, CALLED THE ACROPOLIS, SIT THE REMAINS OF A GROUP OF TEMPLES. THE LARGEST AND MOST FAMOUS IS THE PARTHENON.

GREECE HAS ONE OF THE WORLD'S BIGGEST SHIPPING FLEETS.

TEMPLE OF ATHENA LINDIA AT LINDOS

RHODES

SHAKE MY HAND.

FEWER THAN 175 OF GREECE'S 2,000 ISLANDS ARE INHABITED.

GREEK CULTURE WAS SPREAD ACROSS NORTH AFRICA AND ASIA BY ALEXANDER THE GREAT IN THE 4TH CENTURY B.C.

MEDITERRANEAN SEA

SEA OF CRETE

WE ARE THE LARGEST GREEK ISLAND.

OCTOPUS

ANCIENT GREEK SHIP

CRETE

DOLPHIN

RUINS OF KNOSSOS

WE WERE ONCE THE CENTER OF THE MINOAN CIVILIZATION, WHICH FLOURISHED 3,500 YEARS AGO.

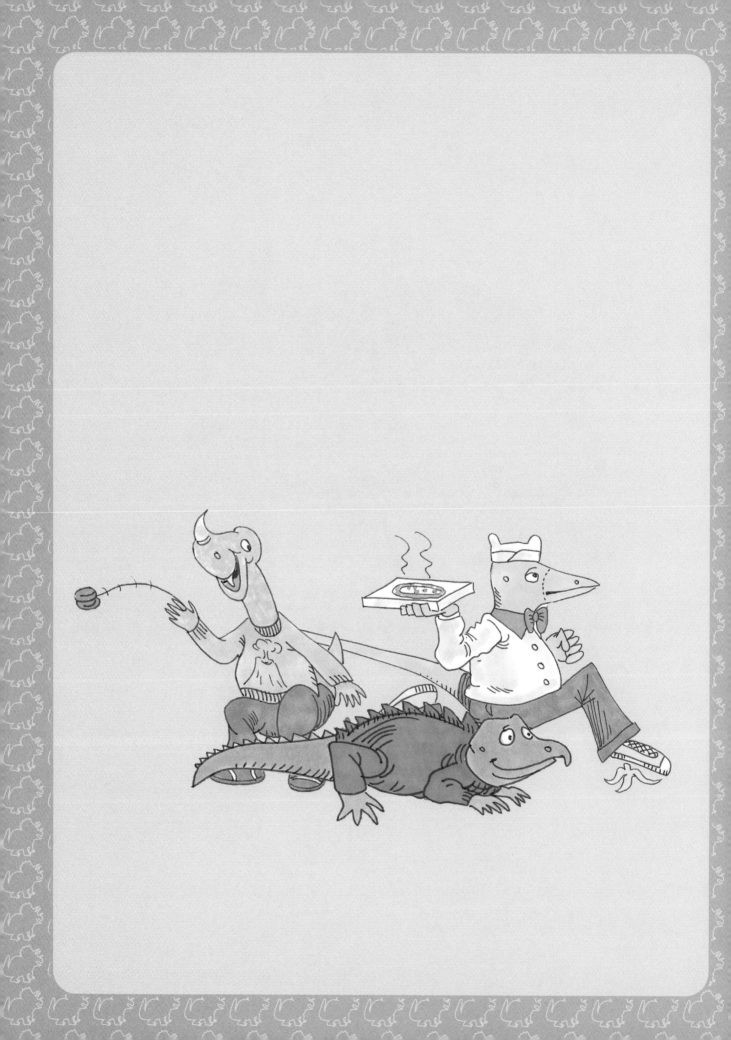

LOOK
& LOOK AGAIN

DINOSAURS

FAST-FOODASAURUS

FIND THESE ITEMS:

- ☐ Banana peel
- ☐ Bell
- ☐ Beret
- ☐ Bones (2)
- ☐ Book
- ☐ Bow tie
- ☐ Broken balloon
- ☐ Cactus
- ☐ Candle
- ☐ Chef
- ☐ Crayon
- ☐ Envelope
- ☐ Eyeglasses
- ☐ Fish (2)
- ☐ Flower
- ☐ Flying bat
- ☐ Football
- ☐ Heart
- ☐ Key
- ☐ Lost sock
- ☐ Mouse hole
- ☐ Mushroom
- ☐ Music note
- ☐ Net
- ☐ Rabbit
- ☐ Saw
- ☐ Scarf
- ☐ Star
- ☐ Sunglasses
- ☐ Tattoo
- ☐ Toothbrush
- ☐ Umbrella
- ☐ Whistle

FAMILY REUNION PORTRAITASAURUS

FIND THESE ITEMS:

- ☐ Baseball
- ☐ Baseball bat
- ☐ Baseball caps (2)
- ☐ Cactus
- ☐ Candle
- ☐ Coffee cup
- ☐ Coffeepot
- ☐ Cookie
- ☐ Dino ordering pizza
- ☐ Egg
- ☐ Eyeglasses
- ☐ Football
- ☐ Fish
- ☐ Flower
- ☐ Heart
- ☐ Horseshoe
- ☐ Mouse
- ☐ Moustache
- ☐ Paintbrush
- ☐ Pear
- ☐ Ring
- ☐ Rollerskate
- ☐ Sleeping dino
- ☐ Stars (2)
- ☐ Straw
- ☐ Yo-yo

SKI-A-SAURUS MOUNTAIN

FIND ALL THE LETTERS
OF THE ALPHABET:

- ☐ A
- ☐ B
- ☐ C
- ☐ D
- ☐ E
- ☐ F
- ☐ G
- ☐ H
- ☐ I
- ☐ J
- ☐ K
- ☐ L
- ☐ M
- ☐ N
- ☐ O
- ☐ P
- ☐ Q
- ☐ R
- ☐ S
- ☐ T
- ☐ U
- ☐ V
- ☐ W
- ☐ X
- ☐ Y
- ☐ Z
- ☐ Baseball hat
- ☐ Flower
- ☐ Heart
- ☐ Pizza delivery dino
- ☐ Star

THE DUNCE-A-SAURUS CLUB

FIND THESE ITEMS:

- ☐ Apple
- ☐ Banana peel
- ☐ Barber pole
- ☐ Baseball bat
- ☐ Birdcage
- ☐ Cactus
- ☐ Capless dino
- ☐ Cupcake
- ☐ Fire hydrant
- ☐ Fish
- ☐ Flower
- ☐ Ghost
- ☐ Golf club
- ☐ Ice-cream cone
- ☐ Kite
- ☐ Mailbox
- ☐ Mouse hole
- ☐ Mustaches (2)
- ☐ Paintbrush
- ☐ Pencil
- ☐ Quarter moon
- ☐ Rabbit
- ☐ Ring
- ☐ Scarf
- ☐ Seal
- ☐ Star
- ☐ Tepee
- ☐ Thermometer
- ☐ Watermelon slice
- ☐ Whale

SHOP-A-HOLIC SAURUS

FIND THESE ITEMS:

- ☐ Arrows (5)
- ☐ Books (2)
- ☐ Bird
- ☐ Broken bulb
- ☐ Bubble gum bubble
- ☐ Cane
- ☐ Cap
- ☐ Coffee cup
- ☐ Earmuffs
- ☐ Fish
- ☐ Football
- ☐ Lost balloon
- ☐ Lost sock
- ☐ Mailbox
- ☐ Music note
- ☐ Newspaper reader
- ☐ Pencil
- ☐ Phonograph
- ☐ Rocking chair
- ☐ Scarves (2)
- ☐ Shoulder bag
- ☐ Star
- ☐ Tires (4)
- ☐ Trash cans (2)
- ☐ Umbrella
- ☐ Vacant store
- ☐ Volcano
- ☐ Water fountain

MT. VOLCANOSAURUS

FIND THESE ITEMS:

- ☐ Automobile
- ☐ Banana
- ☐ Bath brush
- ☐ Beachball
- ☐ Boot
- ☐ Carrot
- ☐ Clothespin
- ☐ Cow
- ☐ Cowboy hat
- ☐ Crayon
- ☐ Daisy
- ☐ Dart
- ☐ Fish
- ☐ Flying bat
- ☐ Football
- ☐ Ghost
- ☐ Hockey stick
- ☐ Humpty Dumpty
- ☐ Keys (2)
- ☐ Kite
- ☐ Lightbulb
- ☐ Mitten
- ☐ Octopus
- ☐ Pumpkins (2)
- ☐ Rabbit
- ☐ Rooster
- ☐ Sand pail
- ☐ Sock
- ☐ Telescope
- ☐ Television
- ☐ Umbrella

HOLLYWOOD-A-SAURUS

FIND THESE ITEMS:

- ☐ Arrows (2)
- ☐ Baseball cap
- ☐ Beret
- ☐ Bones (2)
- ☐ Bouquet of flowers
- ☐ Burned-out bulb
- ☐ Dino ordering pizza
- ☐ Escaped balloon
- ☐ Feather
- ☐ Football
- ☐ Ice-cream cone
- ☐ Hammer
- ☐ Heart
- ☐ Hot dog
- ☐ Lost shoe
- ☐ Microphone
- ☐ Moustache
- ☐ Pearl necklace
- ☐ Pencil
- ☐ Pizza
- ☐ Scissors
- ☐ Screwdriver
- ☐ Stars (2)
- ☐ Sunglasses (2)
- ☐ Telescope
- ☐ Yo-yo

AIRPORT-A-SAURUS

FIND THESE ITEMS:

- ☐ Accordion
- ☐ Arrow
- ☐ Book
- ☐ Bow tie
- ☐ Candy cane
- ☐ Crown
- ☐ Eyeglasses
- ☐ Flying carpet
- ☐ Flying elephant
- ☐ Flying fish
- ☐ Flying saucer
- ☐ Football
- ☐ Hat box
- ☐ Heart
- ☐ Hot-air balloon
- ☐ Hot dog
- ☐ Ice-cream pop
- ☐ Kite
- ☐ Paper airplane
- ☐ Periscope
- ☐ Pizza box
- ☐ Propellers (2)
- ☐ Roller skates
- ☐ Sailor cap
- ☐ Star
- ☐ Straw
- ☐ Top hat
- ☐ Umbrella
- ☐ Watering can
- ☐ Yo-yo's (2)

SENIOR-CITIZENSAURUS

FIND THESE ITEMS:

- ☐ Anchor
- ☐ Apple
- ☐ Balloon
- ☐ Balls (2)
- ☐ Banana
- ☐ Bow tie
- ☐ Canes (2)
- ☐ Coffeepot
- ☐ Coonskin cap
- ☐ Crown
- ☐ Cup
- ☐ Drum
- ☐ Eyeglasses (4)
- ☐ Feather
- ☐ High-heeled shoes
- ☐ Kite
- ☐ Moustache
- ☐ Neckties (3)
- ☐ Paddle
- ☐ Paintbrush
- ☐ Pencil
- ☐ Pocketbook
- ☐ Propeller
- ☐ Ring
- ☐ Sailboat
- ☐ Sailor cap
- ☐ Skateboard
- ☐ Sunglasses
- ☐ Top hat
- ☐ Turtle
- ☐ Yo-yo

CYBER-SAURUS

FIND THESE ITEMS:

- ☐ Apple core
- ☐ Baseball
- ☐ Baseball bat
- ☐ Cactus
- ☐ Drum
- ☐ Elephant
- ☐ Eyeglasses
- ☐ Fish
- ☐ Flower
- ☐ Ghost
- ☐ Hamburger
- ☐ Hearts (3)
- ☐ Horse
- ☐ Igloo
- ☐ Jester
- ☐ Knitting needle
- ☐ Laundry
- ☐ Lion
- ☐ Mouse
- ☐ Moustache
- ☐ Net
- ☐ Oil can
- ☐ Pencil
- ☐ Penguin
- ☐ Plunger
- ☐ Rabbit

MULTI-CINEMA-SAURUS

FIND THESE ITEMS:

- ☐ "3"
- ☐ Backpack
- ☐ Balloon
- ☐ Bird
- ☐ Bowling bag
- ☐ Burned-out lightbulbs (4)
- ☐ Cane
- ☐ Cell phone
- ☐ Dollar bill
- ☐ Football helmet
- ☐ Gum
- ☐ Hearts (3)
- ☐ Ice-cream pop
- ☐ Lollipop
- ☐ Missing lightbulb
- ☐ Necktie
- ☐ Pillow
- ☐ Rollerskate
- ☐ Scooter
- ☐ Skier
- ☐ Straw
- ☐ Suspenders
- ☐ Toothbrush
- ☐ Top hat
- ☐ Turban
- ☐ Umbrella
- ☐ Volcano

WELCOME TO THE TRIVIA-SAURUS CONVENTION

FIND THESE ITEMS:

- ☐ Astronaut
- ☐ Automobile
- ☐ Banana peel
- ☐ Baseball cap
- ☐ Book
- ☐ Candle
- ☐ Candy cane
- ☐ Cup
- ☐ Eyeglasses
- ☐ Feather
- ☐ Flower
- ☐ Flying bat
- ☐ Ghost
- ☐ Hearts (4)
- ☐ Ice-cream pop
- ☐ Ice skates
- ☐ Jack-o'-lantern
- ☐ Keys (2)
- ☐ Necktie
- ☐ Pencil
- ☐ Pizza delivery dino
- ☐ Pointy beard
- ☐ Propeller
- ☐ Purse
- ☐ Rabbit
- ☐ Rollerskate
- ☐ Scarf
- ☐ Sunglasses
- ☐ Volcano
- ☐ Yo-yo

LUNCH ROOM-A-SAURUS

FIND THESE ITEMS:

- ☐ Alien
- ☐ Backpack
- ☐ Banana peel
- ☐ Bones (2)
- ☐ Broken heart
- ☐ Broom
- ☐ Candle
- ☐ Cell phone
- ☐ Cook
- ☐ Dino ordering pizza
- ☐ Fire hydrant
- ☐ Fish
- ☐ Football helmet
- ☐ Guitar
- ☐ Hammer
- ☐ Ice-cream cone
- ☐ Music note
- ☐ Napkin dispenser
- ☐ Necktie
- ☐ Old tire
- ☐ Paper airplane
- ☐ Pencils (3)
- ☐ Periscope
- ☐ Roller skate
- ☐ Santa cap
- ☐ Skateboard
- ☐ Sock
- ☐ Umbrella
- ☐ Worm

FARM-A-SAURUS

FIND THESE ITEMS:

- ☐ Axe
- ☐ Balloon
- ☐ Candy cane
- ☐ Coffeepot
- ☐ Cow
- ☐ Crayons (3)
- ☐ Crows (7)
- ☐ Dog
- ☐ Duck
- ☐ Empty flowerpot
- ☐ Golf ball
- ☐ Golf club
- ☐ Hoe
- ☐ Horseshoe
- ☐ Ice-cream cone
- ☐ Key
- ☐ Kite
- ☐ Mouse
- ☐ Neckerchief
- ☐ Pear
- ☐ Pencil
- ☐ Pitchfork
- ☐ Rooster
- ☐ Shovel
- ☐ Snake
- ☐ Star
- ☐ Tic-tac-toe
- ☐ Tires (7)
- ☐ Toothbrush
- ☐ Top hat
- ☐ Turtle
- ☐ Watering can
- ☐ Wristwatch

SKATEBOARD-A-SAURUS

FIND THESE ITEMS:

- ☐ Auto
- ☐ Band-aid
- ☐ Banana peel
- ☐ Baseball cap
- ☐ Broken heart
- ☐ Cactus
- ☐ Doghouse
- ☐ Fish (2)
- ☐ Flashlight
- ☐ Ghost
- ☐ Hammer
- ☐ Helmet
- ☐ Lost shoe
- ☐ Motorized board
- ☐ Mushroom
- ☐ Pencil
- ☐ Periscope
- ☐ Pie
- ☐ Pizza
- ☐ Pogo stick
- ☐ Ring
- ☐ Scarf
- ☐ Shark fin
- ☐ Sled
- ☐ Star
- ☐ Three-wheeled board
- ☐ Top hat
- ☐ Turtle
- ☐ Winged board
- ☐ Yo-yo

ROBOTIC-A-SAURUS

FIND THESE ITEMS:

- ☐ Arrow
- ☐ Balloon
- ☐ Banana peel
- ☐ Bow tie
- ☐ Brush
- ☐ Crystal ball
- ☐ Fire hydrant
- ☐ Hammer
- ☐ Hearts (2)
- ☐ Ice-cream cone
- ☐ Ice skates
- ☐ Kite
- ☐ Light bulbs (2)
- ☐ Loose screw
- ☐ Necktie
- ☐ Oil can
- ☐ Pencils (2)
- ☐ Pizza
- ☐ Roller skates
- ☐ Satellite dish
- ☐ Shoulder bag
- ☐ Star
- ☐ Sunglasses
- ☐ Telescope
- ☐ Umbrella
- ☐ Vacuum
- ☐ Yo-yo

SO YOU WANT TO BE A STAR-A-SAURUS

FIND THESE ITEMS:

- [ ] Beret
- [ ] Bird
- [ ] Bottle
- [ ] Bow ties (2)
- [ ] Box
- [ ] Candle
- [ ] Clipboard
- [ ] Crown
- [ ] Dracula-saurus
- [ ] Drum
- [ ] Flower
- [ ] Fork
- [ ] Frying pan
- [ ] Ghost
- [ ] Heart
- [ ] Medal
- [ ] Mustaches (2)
- [ ] Pearl necklace
- [ ] Pencils (2)
- [ ] Periscope
- [ ] Pointy beards (2)
- [ ] Scarves (3)
- [ ] Stars (2)
- [ ] Sunglasses (3)
- [ ] Sword
- [ ] Ten-gallon hat
- [ ] Ticket
- [ ] Tic-tac-toe
- [ ] Top hat
- [ ] Walking stick

MARATHON-A-SAURUS

FIND THESE ITEMS:

- ☐ Automobile
- ☐ Axe
- ☐ Bird
- ☐ Bowling ball
- ☐ Cactus
- ☐ Cell phone
- ☐ Coffeepot
- ☐ Cup
- ☐ Fire hydrant
- ☐ Fish
- ☐ Jack-o'-lantern
- ☐ Jester's cap
- ☐ Key
- ☐ Kite
- ☐ Lost baseball caps (2)
- ☐ Moustache
- ☐ Pencil
- ☐ Rolling pin
- ☐ Skateboard
- ☐ Socks (2)
- ☐ Star
- ☐ Straw
- ☐ Telescope
- ☐ Tent
- ☐ Traffic light
- ☐ Tulip
- ☐ Turtle
- ☐ Volcano

HARD HAT-A-SAURUS

FIND THESE ITEMS:

- ☐ Arrows (5)
- ☐ Astronaut
- ☐ Balloons (3)
- ☐ Banana peel
- ☐ Bicycle
- ☐ Book
- ☐ Bowling ball
- ☐ Clothes line
- ☐ Comb
- ☐ Cow
- ☐ Fish
- ☐ Fish bowl
- ☐ Football
- ☐ Hearts (2)
- ☐ Igloo
- ☐ Lunchbox
- ☐ Moose head
- ☐ Mouse
- ☐ Paint can
- ☐ Sail
- ☐ Saw
- ☐ Scarf
- ☐ Snake
- ☐ Socks (2)
- ☐ Sunglasses
- ☐ Tepee
- ☐ Thermometer
- ☐ Top hat
- ☐ Turtle
- ☐ Used tire
- ☐ Wheelbarrow

THE FAMOUS STORY OF FRANKENSAURUS

FIND THESE ITEMS:

- ☐ Alarm clock
- ☐ Axe
- ☐ Banana peel
- ☐ Band-aids (2)
- ☐ Baseball bat
- ☐ Baseball cap
- ☐ Bow and arrow
- ☐ Bowling ball
- ☐ Candle
- ☐ Cupcake
- ☐ Dead flower
- ☐ Drum
- ☐ Eyeglasses
- ☐ Fire hydrant
- ☐ Fish
- ☐ Football
- ☐ Heart
- ☐ Knitting needles
- ☐ Lollipop
- ☐ Oil can
- ☐ Paddle
- ☐ Paper airplane
- ☐ Pencils (2)
- ☐ Periscope
- ☐ Pizza
- ☐ Rolling pin
- ☐ Saw
- ☐ Scissors
- ☐ Screwdriver
- ☐ Sunglasses
- ☐ Tape
- ☐ Thermometer
- ☐ Tic-tac-toe
- ☐ Turtle
- ☐ Yo-yo

DINO-WRESTLING
IS REALLY HUGE!

FIND THESE ITEMS:

- ☐ Band-Aid
- ☐ Baseball caps (3)
- ☐ Baseball glove
- ☐ Basketball
- ☐ Bow tie
- ☐ Camera
- ☐ Drinking straw
- ☐ Egg
- ☐ Envelope
- ☐ Flowers
- ☐ Harmonica
- ☐ Headphones (2)
- ☐ Heart
- ☐ Hot dog
- ☐ Ice-cream cone
- ☐ Kite
- ☐ Lost balloons (2)
- ☐ Microphone
- ☐ Necktie
- ☐ Pencils (2)
- ☐ Periscope
- ☐ Scarf
- ☐ Slice of pizza
- ☐ Straw hat
- ☐ Sunglasses
- ☐ Telescope
- ☐ Top hat
- ☐ Yo-yo

THE VOYAGE OF CHRISTOPHER COLUMBUSAURUS

FIND THESE ITEMS:

- ☐ Balloons (3)
- ☐ Barber pole
- ☐ Bird
- ☐ Brushes (2)
- ☐ Bullhorn
- ☐ Candle
- ☐ Chef's hat
- ☐ Fire hydrant
- ☐ Fishing rod
- ☐ Heart
- ☐ Horseshoe
- ☐ Hourglass
- ☐ Ice-cream cone
- ☐ Key
- ☐ Kite
- ☐ Mermaid
- ☐ Periscope
- ☐ Pie
- ☐ Sock
- ☐ Sunglasses
- ☐ Sailor's cap
- ☐ Telescope
- ☐ Tire
- ☐ Umbrella
- ☐ Yo-yo

DINOSAURS IN SPACE

FIND THESE ITEMS:

- ☐ Apple
- ☐ Banana
- ☐ Band-Aid
- ☐ Barber pole
- ☐ Baseball
- ☐ Baseball cap
- ☐ Bow tie
- ☐ Cane
- ☐ Carrot
- ☐ Coffeepot
- ☐ Cups (2)
- ☐ Envelopes (2)
- ☐ Flower pot
- ☐ Garden hose
- ☐ Hammer
- ☐ Hitchhiker
- ☐ Ice-cream cone
- ☐ Key
- ☐ Kite
- ☐ Lost shoe
- ☐ Medal
- ☐ Oil can
- ☐ Pencil
- ☐ Saw
- ☐ Screwdriver
- ☐ Shovel
- ☐ Speaker
- ☐ Telescope
- ☐ Tepee
- ☐ Tic-tac-toe
- ☐ Toothbrush

DINO VACATIONS IN NEW YORK CITY

FIND THESE ITEMS:

- ☐ Banana
- ☐ Bicycle messenger
- ☐ Bone
- ☐ Burned-out bulbs (3)
- ☐ Camera
- ☐ Cane
- ☐ Clipboard
- ☐ Clothespin
- ☐ Crayon
- ☐ Envelope
- ☐ Fire hydrants (3)
- ☐ Fork
- ☐ Ghost
- ☐ Hearts (2)
- ☐ Horseshoe
- ☐ Ice-cream cone
- ☐ In-line skater
- ☐ Jack-o'-lantern
- ☐ Ladder
- ☐ Lost balloon
- ☐ Mouse
- ☐ Paintbrush
- ☐ Paper airplane
- ☐ Party hat
- ☐ Tepee
- ☐ Worm

DINOSAURS IN
KING ARTHUR'S
COURT

FIND THESE ITEMS:

- ☐ Balloon
- ☐ Banana
- ☐ Banana peels (2)
- ☐ Baseball cap
- ☐ Basketball
- ☐ Bell
- ☐ Bird
- ☐ Bone
- ☐ Bow tie
- ☐ Candle
- ☐ Carrot
- ☐ Clothespins (3)
- ☐ Earring
- ☐ Feather
- ☐ Ice-cream cone
- ☐ Jestersaurus
- ☐ Jugglesaurus
- ☐ Light bulb
- ☐ Merlinasaurus
- ☐ Pearl necklace
- ☐ Roller skate
- ☐ Sock
- ☐ Swords (3)
- ☐ Telescope
- ☐ Whale

DINO SUPERHEROES

FIND THESE ITEMS:

- ☐ Arrow
- ☐ Banana peel
- ☐ Bone
- ☐ Cactus
- ☐ Chef's hat
- ☐ Drum
- ☐ Envelope
- ☐ Fish
- ☐ Football
- ☐ Gavel
- ☐ Hammer
- ☐ Heart
- ☐ Hot dog
- ☐ Jack-o'-lantern
- ☐ Key
- ☐ Kite
- ☐ Owl
- ☐ Paper airplane
- ☐ Pencil
- ☐ Rabbit
- ☐ Screwdriver
- ☐ Seal
- ☐ Straw
- ☐ Tack
- ☐ Television
- ☐ Toothbrush
- ☐ Umbrella

WILD WEST TOWN

FIND THESE ITEMS:

- ☐ Arrows (2)
- ☐ Axe
- ☐ Badges (2)
- ☐ Balloons (2)
- ☐ Banana
- ☐ Barrel
- ☐ Bones (2)
- ☐ Bow tie
- ☐ Brush
- ☐ Cactus (2)
- ☐ Candle
- ☐ Cheese
- ☐ Coonskin caps (2)
- ☐ Cup
- ☐ Drums (2)
- ☐ Elephant
- ☐ Eyeglasses
- ☐ Fire hydrant
- ☐ Fish
- ☐ Flower
- ☐ Football
- ☐ Heart
- ☐ Horseshoe
- ☐ Pencil
- ☐ Razor
- ☐ Ring
- ☐ Top hat
- ☐ Worm

PICNIC-A-SAURUS

FIND THESE ITEMS:

- ☐ Arrow
- ☐ Baseball caps (2)
- ☐ Bone
- ☐ Cactus
- ☐ Comb
- ☐ Cell phone
- ☐ Eyeglasses (2)
- ☐ Fish
- ☐ Flower
- ☐ Football
- ☐ Forks (3)
- ☐ Four-leaf clover
- ☐ Frog
- ☐ Ghost
- ☐ Hot dog
- ☐ Lamp
- ☐ Lion
- ☐ Lost kite
- ☐ Lost sunglasses
- ☐ Mushroom
- ☐ Pie
- ☐ Pizza delivery dino
- ☐ Propeller
- ☐ Ring
- ☐ Salt shaker
- ☐ Star
- ☐ Yo-yo

A DAY AT DINO-LAND

FIND THESE ITEMS:

- ☐ Bone
- ☐ Bow tie
- ☐ Fire hydrant
- ☐ Fish
- ☐ Flower
- ☐ Flower pot
- ☐ Football
- ☐ Heart
- ☐ Hot-air balloon
- ☐ Necktie
- ☐ Net
- ☐ Pencil
- ☐ Periscope
- ☐ Pick
- ☐ Pizza delivery dino
- ☐ Plunger
- ☐ Screwdriver
- ☐ Shark fin
- ☐ Shovel
- ☐ Skier
- ☐ Sled
- ☐ Sunglasses
- ☐ Suspenders
- ☐ Tire
- ☐ Turtle

DINO-5...
IN CONCERT

FIND THESE ITEMS:

☐ Accordion
☐ Apple
☐ Arrow
☐ Astronaut
☐ Bandanna
☐ Basketball
☐ Bell
☐ Beret
☐ Cane
☐ Carrot
☐ Crayon
☐ Empty birdcage
☐ Fish
☐ Hearts (3)
☐ Key
☐ Light bulb
☐ Lost balloon
☐ Monocle
☐ Moon face
☐ Moustache
☐ Paintbrush
☐ Pear
☐ Pencil
☐ Pizza delivery dino
☐ Sailor cap
☐ Seal
☐ Straw
☐ Sunglasses
☐ Teapot
☐ Thermometer
☐ Top hat
☐ Whistler

LAST ONE IN IS A
ROTTENSAURUS EGG

FIND THESE ITEMS:

- ☐ Balloons (2)
- ☐ Baseball caps (4)
- ☐ Bird
- ☐ Book
- ☐ Boombox
- ☐ Bone
- ☐ Bowling ball
- ☐ Fire hydrant
- ☐ Flashlight
- ☐ Football
- ☐ Golf club
- ☐ Hammer
- ☐ Horseshoe
- ☐ Ice-cream cone
- ☐ Lamp
- ☐ Mushroom
- ☐ Paper airplane
- ☐ Periscopes (2)
- ☐ Pizza delivery dino
- ☐ Ring
- ☐ Sailor cap
- ☐ Shark fins (2)
- ☐ Starfish
- ☐ Sunglasses (2)
- ☐ Telescope
- ☐ Top hat
- ☐ TV set

SCHOOL-YARDASAURUS

FIND THESE ITEMS:

- ☐ Balloon
- ☐ Banana peel
- ☐ Beret
- ☐ Bones (2)
- ☐ Bow tie
- ☐ Broom
- ☐ Butterfly
- ☐ Camera
- ☐ Coonskin cap
- ☐ Drum
- ☐ Drum major
- ☐ Eyeglasses (2)
- ☐ Fish
- ☐ Heart
- ☐ Hot dog
- ☐ Juggler
- ☐ Kite
- ☐ Lit candle
- ☐ Lollipop
- ☐ Lost cookie
- ☐ Lost sneakers
- ☐ Mailbox
- ☐ Paper airplane
- ☐ Pizza delivery dino
- ☐ Sailor cap
- ☐ Skate
- ☐ Star
- ☐ Sunglasses
- ☐ Tennis racket
- ☐ Tuba
- ☐ Yo-yo

STAND-UP DINO

FIND THESE ITEMS:

- ☐ Airplane
- ☐ Anchor
- ☐ Apple
- ☐ Barrel
- ☐ Baseball bat
- ☐ Binoculars
- ☐ Bone
- ☐ Burned-out bulb
- ☐ Candle
- ☐ Chicken
- ☐ Clothespin
- ☐ Cups (5)
- ☐ Earring
- ☐ Fish (2)
- ☐ Football
- ☐ Heart
- ☐ Hot dog
- ☐ Kite
- ☐ Mailbox
- ☐ Monocle
- ☐ Moustache
- ☐ Pencils (2)
- ☐ Pizza delivery dino
- ☐ Sailboat
- ☐ Sled
- ☐ Sunglasses

MUSEUM-SAURUS

FIND THESE ITEMS:

- [ ] Arrow
- [ ] Astronaut
- [ ] Bib
- [ ] Broom
- [ ] Camera
- [ ] Cane
- [ ] Crack
- [ ] Crown
- [ ] Dart
- [ ] Eyeglasses
- [ ] Fish
- [ ] Flower
- [ ] Golf club
- [ ] Heart
- [ ] Hourglass
- [ ] Menu
- [ ] Moustache
- [ ] Nail
- [ ] Pencils (3)
- [ ] Pizza delivery dino
- [ ] Rock
- [ ] Roll
- [ ] Telescope
- [ ] Toothbrush
- [ ] Top hat
- [ ] Umbrella
- [ ] Volcano
- [ ] Yo-yo

FIND CUPID AMONG THESE CARTOON FAVORITES, AND THESE FUN ITEMS:

- ☐ Balloons (4)
- ☐ Banana peel
- ☐ Baseball
- ☐ Basket
- ☐ Beehive
- ☐ Bone
- ☐ Cactus
- ☐ Candle
- ☐ Cup
- ☐ Feather
- ☐ Flowers (2)
- ☐ Flying bats (2)
- ☐ Hearts (10)
- ☐ Lock
- ☐ Magic lamp
- ☐ Mirror
- ☐ Mushroom
- ☐ Music note
- ☐ Painted egg
- ☐ Piggy bank
- ☐ Pirate
- ☐ Pizzas (2)
- ☐ Tire
- ☐ Top hat
- ☐ Turtle
- ☐ Umbrella

FIND CUPID IN VERONA, AND THESE FUN ITEMS:

- ☐ Baseball cap
- ☐ Bird
- ☐ Bull's-eye
- ☐ Candy cane
- ☐ Duck
- ☐ Fishing pole
- ☐ Football player
- ☐ Frog
- ☐ Hamburger
- ☐ Hot dog
- ☐ Ice skates
- ☐ Key
- ☐ Kites (2)
- ☐ Light bulb
- ☐ Mouse
- ☐ Paper airplane
- ☐ Pie
- ☐ Pillow
- ☐ Propeller
- ☐ Roller skates
- ☐ Saw
- ☐ Skateboard
- ☐ Sock
- ☐ Stars (3)
- ☐ Sunglasses
- ☐ Television

FIND CUPID IN THIS SPOOKY CAVE, AND THESE FUN ITEMS:

- ☐ Balloons (2)
- ☐ Boat
- ☐ Bones (4)
- ☐ Boot
- ☐ Briefcase
- ☐ Broom
- ☐ Candle
- ☐ Dogs (2)
- ☐ Drum
- ☐ Envelope
- ☐ Flowers (3)
- ☐ Football
- ☐ Ghosts (3)
- ☐ Helmets (2)
- ☐ Kite
- ☐ Monsters with horns (4)
- ☐ Mummy
- ☐ Paintbrush
- ☐ Painted eggs (2)
- ☐ Ring
- ☐ Star
- ☐ Sock
- ☐ Turtle
- ☐ Top hat
- ☐ Train engine
- ☐ Umbrella

FIND CUPID AT WASHINGTON'S WEDDING AND THESE FUN ITEMS:

- ☐ Apple
- ☐ Banana peel
- ☐ Bone
- ☐ Bonnet
- ☐ Bowling ball
- ☐ Butterfly
- ☐ Camera
- ☐ Candy cane
- ☐ Chalkboard
- ☐ Crayon
- ☐ Drumstick
- ☐ Egg
- ☐ Feathers (4)
- ☐ Firecracker
- ☐ Fish (2)
- ☐ Hearts (4)
- ☐ Kites (2)
- ☐ Knight
- ☐ Mouse
- ☐ Pizza
- ☐ Rabbits (2)
- ☐ Shovel
- ☐ Snail
- ☐ Socks (3)
- ☐ Surfboard
- ☐ Toaster
- ☐ Umbrella
- ☐ Witch's hats (2)

FIND CUPID IN SHERWOOD FOREST AND THESE FUN ITEMS:

- ☐ Balloon
- ☐ Bell
- ☐ Birdcage
- ☐ Broom
- ☐ Cactus
- ☐ Camel
- ☐ Candle
- ☐ Car
- ☐ Clock
- ☐ Eagle
- ☐ Elephant
- ☐ Feathers (3)
- ☐ Fish (2)
- ☐ Fishing pole
- ☐ Fork
- ☐ Ghosts (2)
- ☐ Gold coin
- ☐ Golf club
- ☐ Humpty Dumpty
- ☐ Igloo
- ☐ Ladder
- ☐ Mice (2)
- ☐ Owl
- ☐ Paintbrush
- ☐ Slingshot
- ☐ Star
- ☐ Sunglasses
- ☐ Turtles (3)

FIND CUPID IN THIS SCENE AND THESE FUN ITEMS:

- ☐ Ant
- ☐ Apple
- ☐ Baseball bat
- ☐ Bears (2)
- ☐ Bone
- ☐ Cat
- ☐ Deer
- ☐ Dog
- ☐ Drum
- ☐ Fish (5)
- ☐ Frog
- ☐ Ghost
- ☐ Guitar
- ☐ Hearts (14)
- ☐ Howling wolf
- ☐ Mouse
- ☐ Pig
- ☐ Porcupine
- ☐ Rabbits (3)
- ☐ Raccoon
- ☐ Skunk
- ☐ Snake in the grass
- ☐ Snake out of the grass
- ☐ Spacecraft
- ☐ Sunflower
- ☐ Windup cowboy

FIND CUPID ON THIS BUSY STREET, AND THESE FUN ITEMS:

- ☐ Banana peel
- ☐ Barrel
- ☐ Basketball hoop
- ☐ Black cat
- ☐ Boat builder
- ☐ Bones (3)
- ☐ Bowling ball
- ☐ Candle
- ☐ Candy cane
- ☐ Chef
- ☐ Firefighter
- ☐ Football player
- ☐ Goat
- ☐ Green wagon
- ☐ Hearts (4)
- ☐ Horses (2)
- ☐ Laundry
- ☐ Music note
- ☐ Newspaper
- ☐ Panda
- ☐ Pole vaulter
- ☐ Red balloon
- ☐ Skateboard
- ☐ Top hat
- ☐ Torch
- ☐ Umbrellas (2)

FIND CUPID IN THE CROCKETT'S YARD, AND THESE FUN ITEMS:

- [ ] Apple
- [ ] Axe
- [ ] Ball
- [ ] Baskets (2)
- [ ] Bears (3)
- [ ] Beaver
- [ ] Bee
- [ ] Bone
- [ ] Broom
- [ ] Candle
- [ ] Chicken
- [ ] Child's wagon
- [ ] Cricket
- [ ] Dogs (2)
- [ ] Goldilocks
- [ ] Hearts (3)
- [ ] Lion
- [ ] Lost hat
- [ ] Moose
- [ ] Pinocchio
- [ ] Rain barrel
- [ ] Rake
- [ ] Shovel
- [ ] Snake
- [ ] Squirrel
- [ ] Tugboat
- [ ] Turkey
- [ ] Wagon wheel

FIND CUPID AMONG THE GRUESOME GHOULIES AND THESE FUN ITEMS:

- ☐ Baseball bat
- ☐ Baseball cap
- ☐ Bird's nest
- ☐ Blue moon
- ☐ Bones (2)
- ☐ Broken TV set
- ☐ Candles (3)
- ☐ Chef's hat
- ☐ Count Dracula
- ☐ Eyeglasses (2)
- ☐ Flowers (3)
- ☐ Ghosts (4)
- ☐ Hearts (4)
- ☐ Hockey stick
- ☐ Jack-o'-lanterns (2)
- ☐ Key
- ☐ Lollipop
- ☐ Mitten
- ☐ Mouse
- ☐ Octopus
- ☐ Piggy bank
- ☐ Pyramid
- ☐ Roller skates
- ☐ Sailor's cap
- ☐ Sled
- ☐ Sock
- ☐ Tent
- ☐ Worms (2)

FIND CUPID ON THIS MOONLIT NIGHT, AND THESE FUN ITEMS:

- ☐ Arrows (2)
- ☐ Axe
- ☐ Bearded man
- ☐ Bell
- ☐ Bone
- ☐ Bowling ball
- ☐ Broken heart
- ☐ Broom
- ☐ Comb
- ☐ Cradle
- ☐ Dog
- ☐ Flying bat
- ☐ Frying pan
- ☐ Hot dog
- ☐ Lost boot
- ☐ Owl
- ☐ Pencil
- ☐ Pie
- ☐ Rabbit
- ☐ Santa Claus
- ☐ Scissors
- ☐ Skateboard
- ☐ Squirrel
- ☐ Telescope
- ☐ Unicorn

FIND CUPID AMONG THE FALLING LEAVES, AND THESE FUN ITEMS:

- ☐ Ball of yarn
- ☐ Balloon
- ☐ Banana peel
- ☐ Bat under a hat
- ☐ Bottle
- ☐ Broken dish
- ☐ Butterfly
- ☐ Cat
- ☐ Crayon
- ☐ Drum
- ☐ Duck
- ☐ Fishing pole
- ☐ Football player
- ☐ Golf ball
- ☐ Goose
- ☐ Hammer
- ☐ Hoe
- ☐ Igloo
- ☐ Key
- ☐ Kite
- ☐ Knife
- ☐ Paper airplane
- ☐ Pigs (2)
- ☐ Pumpkin
- ☐ Rat in a cap
- ☐ Skateboard
- ☐ Umpire

CUPID HAS SHOT 16 ARROWS.

FIND ALL OF THE ARROWS, AND THESE FUN ITEMS:

- ☐ Balloons (2)
- ☐ Bone
- ☐ Flowers (12)
- ☐ Moon face
- ☐ Mouse
- ☐ Stars (5)
- ☐ Wreath